BIG SURF

DEEP DIVES

AND THE ISLANDS

My Life in the Ocean

RICKY GRIGG

Published by
Editions Limited
P.O. Box 10150
Honolulu, Hawai'i 96816

First Edition 1998

ISBN 0-915013-20-7
LIBRARY OF CONGRESS CATALOG
CARD NO. 97-78465

Duke Kahanamoku photograph on page 36
used with the permission of the Outrigger
Duke Kahanamoku Foundation and DPKL.

Design and production assistance by
Ricky Grigg, Barbara Pope Book Design,
and Diane Nakashima
Back cover painting and woodcuts
by Raina Lai-Lin Grigg, 1998

Printed in Hong Kong

To the sea, in all its splendor

Ron Church photo

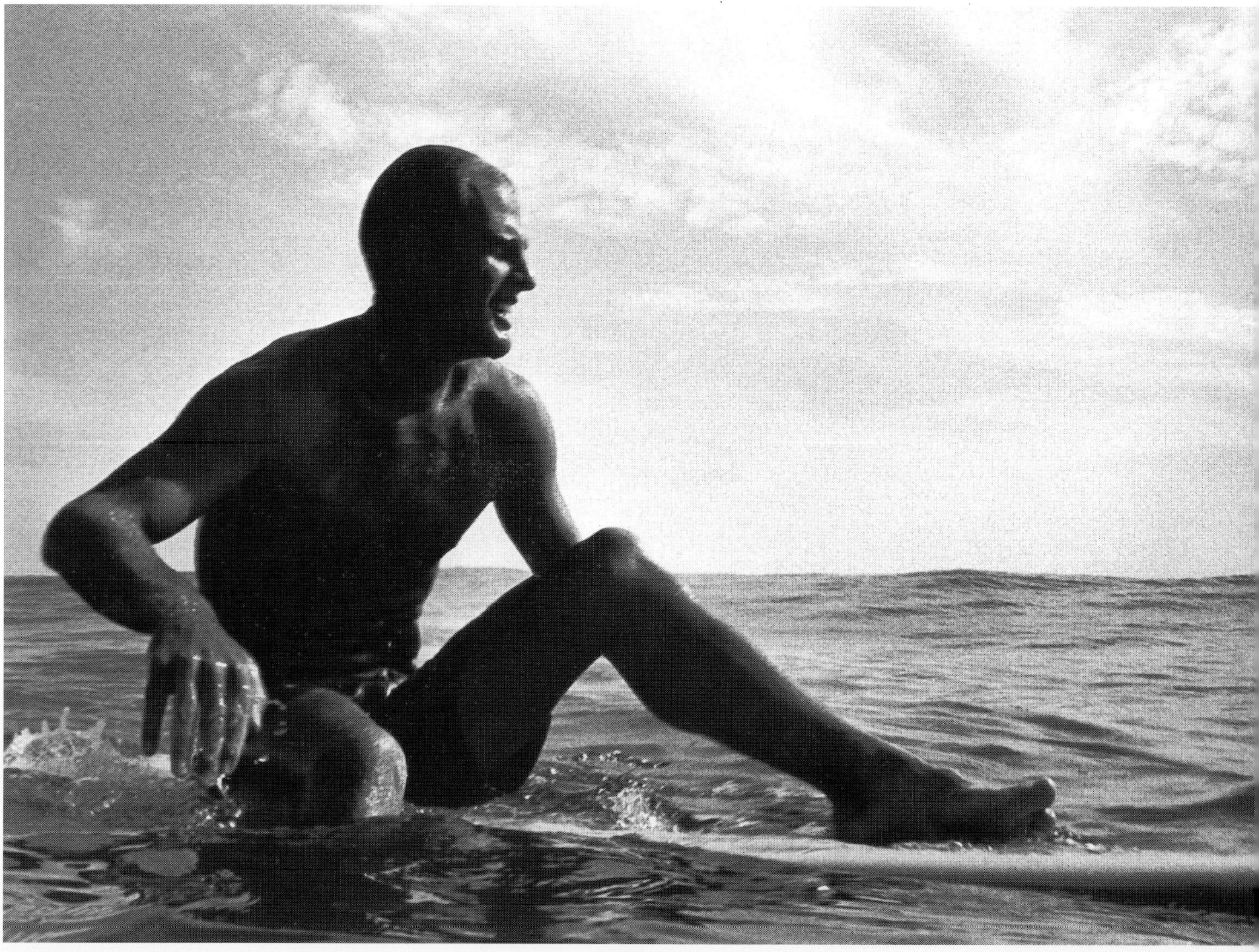

CONTENTS

Ricky bodysurfing
Sunset Beach.
Bud Browne photo.

FOREWORD

One of the great images of twentieth-century surfing is the bespectacled Ricky Grigg at the water's edge, checking the surf. He could go either way at that point—into the office, where he is one of the world's most respected oceanographers, or into the sea, where his big-wave riding is the stuff of legend. Most of us are lucky to be known for a single moment or accomplishment, perhaps a body of work. Grigg is an institution in separate worlds, and he will be remembered not as one person, but two.

Grigg claims to have slowed down as he enters his sixties, but you would never know it. While continuing to craft some of today's most detailed and thought-provoking studies on coral reefs, Grigg still loves big waves—a roaring 12-foot day at Sunset, a windsurf at Outside Backyards, a timely visit to O'ahu's south shore during a huge summer swell. There is a timeless quality to Ricky Grigg—Richard, as he's known in scientific circles—because he never outgrew surfing or his love for the ocean. At once a hardened realist and hopeless romantic, he has asked only one thing of life: to make it count for something. He has succeeded mightily.

Grigg's story takes the reader on a journey through the pioneer days of surfing on the North Shore, where Grigg was a standout at Waimea Bay and an innovator at Sunset Beach. But it begins much earlier, in Santa Monica, California, the spawning ground for many great watermen of the 1940s, '50s, and '60s. Ricky caught his first wave at Malibu Point, in tandem with his idol, Buzzy Trent. He won the first Catalina-to-Manhattan paddleboard race, 32 miles, at the age of eighteen in 1955. He became known for his "hotdog" surfing, his diving ability, and his studious nature, leading him to Stanford University and eventually to the Scripps Institution of Oceanography in San Diego. He managed somehow to hold his contrasting lifestyles in balance.

If there is a single episode that sums up his life, it was in February

1967, when a pale Rick Grigg stepped off the plane at Honolulu International Airport after being invited to the prestigious Duke Kahanamoku contest. Locked in his studies back in California, Grigg had not surfed the North Shore in two years. He was about to turn thirty. The field was loaded with storied surfers, including Greg Noll, Mike Doyle, Jock Sutherland, and Eddie Aikau. The waves were a stunning, terrifying 15 feet, a day once described by Noll and George Downing as the best Sunset they had ever seen. Grigg did not just participate—he charged into the surf and won the contest, in its day the highest possible honor in surfing.

Like all the great surfers, Grigg had style. You could spot him on a big wave from a hundred yards away, arching his back and throwing his arms

Dr. Richard Grigg displays a new species of deep coral of the genus Paragorgia, *collected at 1,200 feet deep off Kaena Point, Oʻahu.*

into the air, joyously, at a time when others were gripped by fear. "That is the way I'll always remember Ricky," Noll once said. "A lot of us had a barroom-brawl attitude about catching the biggest wave. It was almost vicious. With Ricky, it was more of a playful thing. He had a real love affair with the ocean."

Grigg knew how it felt to take a 40-foot drop at Waimea. He was among the first surfers to challenge second-reef Pipeline in the early 1960s. He knew the splendor of free-diving 100 feet below the surface, in search of dinner or coral reef discoveries, or leaping off his board at the top of a giant wave to feel the sensation of bodysurfing it for a few choice moments. To this day, he knows and experiences fear. Like a select few, he leaves it behind in the wild, open ocean. Out there, he is in his element.

In my first encounters with Grigg he was typically cordial, matter-of-fact, almost awkward. He has the demeanor and precise elocution of a scientist, and for those expecting bawdy, rip-roaring yarns, the experience of meeting him can be disappointing. In time, however, Grigg's complete persona came to life. He told of living his childhood dream as a South Seas pearl diver, sailing the oceans of Polynesia, dancing the nights away with lovely, dark-skinned maidens. He spoke of the chance encounter that led him to Maria Tugaoen, his charming wife, "my Tahitian princess," as he calls her. With familiarity came trust, and the stories he shared with me grew more expansive. Each was a treasure. There are not many people who can kick back with Buffalo Keaulana and the boys at Mākaha in the morning, then drive in to Honolulu to offer a mathematical explanation of wave velocity at the University of Hawai'i in the afternoon. And Grigg, a self-styled loner with a penchant for honesty and an intolerance for environmental propaganda, generally saves his insights for the company of friends. That is why his life story is so welcome. He takes the sad, old stereotype of the dropped-out, mindless surfer and shatters it into little pieces.

Several of Grigg's surfing contemporaries are sharing their stories these days. It is a time to reflect on a magical era in surfing and the people who made it happen. Grigg does that, generously devoting many pages to the big-wave riders he respects most. But the heart of this book reveals a man of high contrast. A surfing professor. A full-fledged adult who never grew up. No nonsense, but a heart of gold. And more than anything, a true original.

Bruce Jenkins
Sportswriter
San Francisco Chronicle

CHILDREN OF THE SEA

by John Craven, former Dean of Marine Programs, University of Hawai'i

All life began in the sea and all terrestrial animals are merely adaptations of primordial marine creatures. The human animal, for example, is a marine mammal from conception through birth.

In 1965 I found myself the manager of the U.S. Navy Sea Lab Program. The mission was to adapt children of the shallow seas to become aquanauts of the deep—100, 200 and 600 feet or more.

Empirical knowledge of the ocean was a mandatory pre-requisite for the aquanauts. Grigg's knowledge in this regard was premier among the Sea Lab participants. His research provided the insight for a breakthrough in understanding of fish aggregation around artificial structures. Years later, in Hawai'i, his research on drowned coral reefs led him to discovering the Darwin Point.

No other scientist could have had this insight had he not been a child of the ocean from birth. The poet Lord Byron once described people thus born:

From a boy I wanton'd with thy breakers—they to me were a delight; and if the freshening sea made them a terror—'twas a pleasing fear, for I was, as it were, a child of thee, and I trusted to thy billows far and near, and laid my hand upon thy mane— as I do here.

An over-the-falls wipeout at Mākaha. The splash behind my feet is my board. Coming up for air after this one took about twenty seconds. Edwin Kaneshiro photo.

1 COMING UP FOR AIR

We come, we know not from whence,
we go, we know not where.
Only the sea endures,
and it does not remember.

Frederick O'Brien
WHITE SHADOWS IN THE SOUTH SEAS

I've been coming up for air my whole life: from surfing wipeouts, from skin diving, from ocean swims, from SCUBA dives, from living under the sea, from dives in submarines, and from various research jobs as an oceanographer. In a more figurative sense, I also come up for air to slow down—to pull out of the fast lane, reflect, and ask, "What's it all about?" In this book, I address this question and in the process tell the story of my life. Like all of us, it has been a search for meaning and also for fun. Surfing taught me that it is all right to have fun. But of course there is more—a lot more. The quest is to be your ideal self, to discover who you are, where you are going, and why. Socrates said, "Know thyself," and that "an unexamined life is not worth living." Intuitively, most people know this commonsense rule. Yet it seems to be a law of life universally ignored. Most of us are so preoccupied rushing headlong down life's free-way that few stop long enough to come up for air and face the question, Who am I?

The lifelong adventure that is the story of my life explains how, along the way, I answered the "Who am I?" question. In that sense this book is autobiographical; on another level, though, it is a story of romance—my romance with the ocean. The ocean has always been the medium of my life. It seems almost to course through my veins, perhaps not unlike a distant ancestor who breathed seawater through its gills. It seems to be a distant memory, a subconscious linkage, so deeply submerged it is almost forgotten. Like many other urges and passions, it is there but invisible, encoded in our genes after millions of years' evolution from tadpoles up through the ladder of primate history—many instincts learned and tucked away in deep recesses, now all but inaccessible without exceptional effort to pull them from memory. Life often requires us to reach deep within ourselves to touch these primordial lessons learned from generations past.

One place we see this dramatized is in sports, especially at their ultimate level in the Olympic Games. Take Carl Lewis' third and last jump to qualify for the finals of the 1996 Games in Atlanta. That jump was almost 3 feet longer than his first two attempts. The next day, Lewis went on to win the gold medal with a jump 8 inches longer than the night before, a storybook finish to a lifetime of competition. An example of a more grueling feat is Joan Benoit's race to make the U.S. 1984 Olympic marathon team. Her run took place seventeen days after knee surgery. In a gutsy, near-miraculous performance, Joan won that race and followed it three months later with a decisive victory in the Olympic final. History is full of examples like these, yet all are rare moments in the life of any given individual. These are moments that show a soul-deep spirit. My brief moment in time came in the winter of 1967 when I won the Duke Kahanamoku Invitational World Surfing Contest at Sunset Beach, Hawai'i.

My mom, Gena, with my sister, Robin, and me in Santa Monica, 1946

Athletics, of course, is only one way to get in touch with yourself, and it's not the winning that matters. Most people agree that what is important is the struggle to achieve. Dostoyevsky expressed it eloquently: "Character is built on the debris of your despair." Struggle, in fact, is inherent in all survival. It is the centerpiece of Charles Darwin's theory of natural selection. Human beings are the product of that selection, and understanding that provides a source of insight into yourself, a window into your soul.

I began surfing when I was nine years old, when my family consisted of my mom, Gena, my sister, Robin, and my dog, Duke. I grew up on the beach in California and my heroes were the lifeguards—the watermen who surfed, swam, paddled, rowed, and dived. They lived by the sea. Their inspiration was my inspiration. Watermen and the ocean were complementary images for me, guideposts along the way.

From a young surfer on the California coast, I gradually evolved into a student of the ocean. Aside from the fun of riding waves, I was always curious about how the ocean worked—where waves come from, what causes them, when I could expect their arrival, and a million other questions. Surfing started me on an endless pursuit of knowledge about the sea. It is a pursuit that constantly builds on itself: The more you know, the more questions you have. Being a surfer helps you become a better oceanographer. Going surfing is like going on a science field trip where you might learn about weather, tide, currents, waves, changes in ocean temperature, and varieties of marine life from jellyfish to sharks. There always seems to be a new lesson to learn. And being an oceanographer makes you a better surfer. For one thing, you often know when and where the surf will be up, even though you may be too busy to go surfing.

A Philosophy of Life

My lifelong involvement with the ocean has helped me formulate a basic philosophy of life. My first principle is "Follow your instincts." To do this, you must look within yourself, deep down, and pull up your feelings. It may sound simple, but dealing squarely with your feelings can be difficult. We often are taught to compromise, to follow society's rules and pressures and the Puritan work ethic, putting "success" ahead of happiness.

The second rule that has guided me as I've slid along the face of life's wave is "Live with integrity." That means being honest and respectful. Being honest—calling it the way it is—can be brutal. Many people regard the truth as whatever they want to believe. Those are the people who are "sometimes right but never in doubt." I have never been too popular with this group, but that's not to say it makes me right. Honesty does not always provide answers. It prevents me from making up answers, though, and helps me recognize answers that others have simply made up. Being respectful—giving the other guy his due—has not been as easy for me as being honest. Growing up in the early days of board surfing, I discovered there were no rules out in the waves. Out there, the rules were invented by the surfers. In the beginning, you could get away with almost anything, but gradually, over time, the tooth-and-claw of life slowly determined the difference between right and wrong. As a young surfer, I sometimes failed to show others proper respect, but as time went on, and as I observed rule-breakers even more flagrant than I, a change slowly took hold in my mind. Order gradually replaced chaos. I learned that respect for others is a form of integrity.

On a more philosophical note, surfing has helped me develop a balance in my life and to understand the nature of reality—that there is a duality in life as well as reality. I address these concepts more thoroughly in chapter 19, so I'll only briefly mention them here. The duality of life refers to a balance that for me results in combining the physical with the intellectual. The duality of reality involves two basic ways to define reality—what actually is (matter and energy) and what appears to be (ideas). For ideas to be correct, they must be constrained by the truth.

My last rule or motto is "Keep surfing." Surfing keeps you in touch with your soul and your basic instincts. It also helps you maintain fantastically good health; it invigorates your body while relaxing your mind. Surfing helps you understand yourself. Consider, for example, a 30-foot wave. You take off on it because you want to, or you don't because you don't. Your instincts decide. Surfing helps you follow your heart and become your ideal self.

So what does all this have to do with my life story? Through surfing, and later in my life by studying the sea, the ocean became a consummate

First photo of me surfing, when I was about ten years old

teacher. It shaped my body and mind, my personality, my philosophy, my view of life, my persona. To me, the ocean represents the truth. It has given me some simple rules to live by, to make choices with, and to measure the consequences of my choices. For me, to seek the truth is to search for the essence of life. Survival. Our ancestors knew this on the plains of Africa. In the ocean, the truth is all that there is. You either survive or you don't.

My purpose in explaining my ocean philosophy and my experience, both as a surfer and as a marine scientist, is to reveal the extent to which the ocean has shaped my being. It truly has been a romance with the ocean—a search for adventure, fun, truth, and meaning. My happiness has come from the freedom to surf and the struggle to know, achieve, and survive. So let me ask you to take a breath and go back down and begin all the chapters of my life.

Wayne Levin photograph, 1990

2 A TOTAL OCEAN LIFE

I do not know what I am to the world,
but to myself, I am but a small boy,
playing on the seashore, searching for
an ever more perfect pebble or seashell,
while before me lies the great ocean of truth.

Sir Isaac Newton

I grew up in Santa Monica, California. Our first house was in Santa Monica Canyon, about a mile from the beach. One day when I was about two years old, my mother took my sister, Robin, and me to the beach. That afternoon I was playing at the water's edge when a wave rushed up the shore and totally engulfed me. The backwash from the wave tumbled me over and dragged me into a deep, over-my-head shoreline trough. Robin, who was five, immediately jumped to her feet, dashed into the water, and rescued me from drowning. It was my first close call with the ocean.

Soon afterward, Mom had me in waterwings and dog paddling back and forth in the pool at the Santa Monica Beach Club. Swimming lessons in the pool kept me out of the ocean for several years. When I was six, we moved down to the beach into an old mansion my grandfather bought us for $7,000. The house had been built in 1907 by the movie star Mary Pickford, but it had been neglected and, by 1943, was pretty run down. The house was about two blocks south of the Santa Monica Pier, right on the boardwalk next to Muscle Beach. Every summer the beach was packed with locals and tourists. When I was about seven, I set up a little shoeshine stand on the boardwalk in front of our house. Military guys from the Chase Hotel a few doors away were my regular customers until one day I polished a pair of tan shoes red. That ended that.

Next door was a hamburger joint owned by Honest John, a "professional" wrestler. Before long Robin and I had renamed him Dishonest John. He had a waxed handle-bar mustache 5 inches long, and he was almost as big around as he was tall. Watching him wrestle was like watching one of the Three Stooges go against Godzilla. He alternated between one or the other of these personalities, depending on who had been chosen to "win" or "lose" that night. Honest John rented surf-riders

My two best friends: my 8'6" Quigg and my dog, Duke

Playing on the beach at the Santa Monica Beach Club, about the age when the big wave pulled me in

19

Shining shoes on the boardwalk with my dog, Rags

(air mattresses were the Boogie Boards of the day) to the public, which he stacked against the white picket fence in front of our house. One day my Mom issued a final warning to Honest John: Remove the surf-riders. When he refused and laughed at her, Mom hooked up a garden hose, turned it on full blast, and marched next door. My little mom almost drowned Honest John. Our fence was free of surf-riders from that day forward.

In contrast to Honest John, Mom was about as straight as any human being could be. She used to tell me that honesty was the only true measure of a person. My parents divorced when I was about three, and I never knew my dad. Mom did both the mothering and the fathering. On one hand, she was very romantic, even spacy—she was an artist, and her dreams extended beyond the normal senses in a Zen sort of way. She followed her heart, her impulses, her intuition. For me, the natural laws of the ocean, to which I was beginning to bond, seemed to carry the same message. The flip side of Mom was completely pragmatic. This was especially true when it came to education and the work ethic. I could never have become a beach bum.

Muscle Beach in those days was a circus, a mecca for all kinds of people—tourists, bums, bathing beauties, and various weirdos. All the permutations of life were on display. Every summer brought parades, beauty pageants, and all kinds of contests—weight lifting, beach acrobatics, volleyball, gymnastics. I was like a kid in a candy store. Muscle Beach was an amusement park with swings and rings and weight-lifting platforms, all the paraphernalia of a permanent carnival. Hamburger stands and cafes with candy apples and cotton candy lined the boardwalk. Old men sat around all day, playing chess under the date palm trees. I watched them for hours and in the process learned how to play chess. The Santa Monica Pier was right next to Muscle Beach, extending out over the ocean about a quarter-mile to sea. It was fronted by a long breakwater, which provided safe anchorage for about a hundred boats. The pier was a good place to fish and check out the waterfront, the fishermen, the yachties, the tourists, and the girls. All of this was my front yard.

Getting Wet

Back then surfers weren't around yet, only bodysurfers and beachgoers. The closest anyone ever came to surfing was splashing around in the waves with air mattresses and wind-bags (pillow cases blown up and tied off), which required no particular skill. It was during these early years in the 1940s that I learned to surf. At first I just bodysurfed and hung around the lifeguard towers. One guard in particular, Buzzy Trent, took a liking to me. Actually, he liked my dog, Duke. Duke always chased after red towels, seizing and shaking them in his mouth. Before long Buzzy had Duke trained to charge a red towel like a bull, and together they passed hours in front of his tower, Buzzy pretending he was a matador. As the

My mom—my guiding light—in her late thirties

A parade and beauty contest on the boardwalk in front of our house at Muscle Beach, 1948

21

days went by, Duke and I gradually became Buzzy Trent's mascots. My "surfing" was limited to catching the whitewater on tiny waves on Buzzy Trent's lifeguard board.

Learning to paddle around the Santa Monica Pier

As I grew older, surfing seemed to suit me best and became my primary sport. In school I was smaller than the football guys and other jocks. I was agile but not very fast. And I wasn't particularly tough. When I turned out for freshman football in high school, I was flattened the first day out trying to catch a pass. A linebacker with a size 18 neck put it right through my stomach. My career in other sports, too, was fairly lackluster. I competed in swimming, but always finished second or third or worse. I was too short and uncoordinated for basketball. For wrestling, I was too weak. For track, too slow. But surfing worked for me. My legs were short, giving me a low center of gravity, and I had lots and lots of endurance. I could paddle forever without getting tired—swimming for my board was never a problem. And I could hold my breath for more than three minutes. Greg Noll and I used to have breath-holding contests. Greg would pass out before he would let me beat him. Surfing, though, was not a competitive sport, at least not back then. Surfing did not have a first team, a coach, pressure, or cheering crowds. You did your own thing. It fit my personality perfectly.

My diving career began under the Santa Monica Pier. I discovered a sand-dollar bed there, and set up a stand next to Honest John selling dried sand dollars to tourists. In my early teens, I grew bolder and began diving the breakwater at night. With a couple of buddies, we jury-rigged a car headlight packed in grease and hooked it up with a cable to a 12-volt battery. Buzzy let me use one of the lifeguard dories to float the battery and one or two tenders while I dragged the boat behind me, diving with the light to spot and grab lobsters. Some nights we got a dozen or more "bugs," as they were called, and soon I was selling chilled lobster cocktails at my stand.

The Romance Begins

I began developing a philosophy of a total ocean life very early on. I remember one day galloping to an afternoon matinee in my cowboy suit. I checked my toy gun at the box office and laid down a quarter for a ticket. The girl selling tickets informed me that there would be no cowboy movie that day. Instead, a movie called *Drums of Pago Pago* was playing. I was disappointed, but because I was already there, why not check it out? As it turned out, the movie changed my life. It was about pearl diving in Samoa. A white slave trader was forcing natives to dive ever deeper and retrieve lustrous, precious pearls from the clutches of giant clams while evading the jaws of circling sharks. The backdrop was palm trees, coral reefs, and beautiful exotic native girls. It was cornball bunk as only Hollywood can produce, but it planted a seed in me that would later become a passion. It was the beginning of my romance with the ocean.

Jo and Ben, my godmother and mentor, clowning around at a costume party

My mom's best friend was Jo Lathwood. Jo and her husband, Ben Masselink, lived at the mouth of Santa Monica Canyon. We often visited them in their small apartment next to the beach, enjoying dinner and listening to their tales of the South Pacific Islands or the Caribbean. Jo and Ben spent about six months every winter touring islands—diving, fishing, painting, and writing. Jo was the artist and Ben was the writer. Their stories and photographs nourished the seed that would one day produce my own adventures in the tropical world.

My first adventure was to be Hawaiʻi, in 1953, when my Mom agreed to let her sixteen-year-old spend the summer in Honolulu. With my earnings from shining shoes and selling sand dollars from summers past, I bought an airline ticket and had $300 in cash left over. I arrived knowing a couple of older surfers from California who were living in Waikīkī. Walter Hoffman agreed to rent me a bed in his garage, but I soon had my own room in a classic old hotel called Fromm's Rooms, one block from the beach at Waikīkī. The rent was $22 a month. Surfing Waikīkī in 1953 was totally mellow. As I think back on it, I cannot remember a single overcrowded wave. It was paradise. My day consisted of a three-hour session in the morning, lunch at Umbrella's for 25 cents (five rice balls and hot gravy), a nap under a coconut tree, and then three more hours in the afternoon surfing Queen's or Canoes. That summer I met Bobbie

23

Richard Kauo styling at Waikīkī, in the early 1950s. Scoop Suzuki photo.

The surf shack at Malibu with a bunch of the regulars checking out the surf. Left to right: Don Drazen, Mike Stevens, my sister Robin, Dave Rochlen, Tom Carpenter, Peter Lawford, Molly Dunn, and Tim Lyons. Peter Lawford became a movie star. Dave Rochlen moved to Hawaiʻi and founded Surfline Hawaii. My sister, Robin, also migrated to Hawaiʻi, where she now owns a ranch on the Big Island. Joe Quigg photo.

24

Patterson, Joey Cabell, Rabbit Kekai, and Richard Kauo. They were all super hotdoggers, particularly on what was known then as the hot-curl board. Instead of a fin for steering, the hot-curl board had a V-shaped bottom near the tail, making it extremely easy to do a standing island pullout: standing on the nose of the board and pulling out of a wave by spinning the front of the board through the back of the curling wave. The tail swung around with almost no resistance. It was cool and very stylish. When I returned to California in September, I had learned a bag of tricks that no one on the coast had ever seen.

Surf and School

Back in California, with another year of high school to finish, I received an ultimatum from my mom: Finish school or lose your surfboard. By school, she meant college. She practically made me sign an oath in blood and determined the shape of my next few years—more study and less surf.

A NEW ERA IN SURFING
by Joe Quigg

Ricky Grigg was just a kid when many of the innovations in surfboard making were taking place on the California Coast during the late 1940s and '50s. Probably the most well-known surfer and board builder up to that time was Bob Simmons, riding and pushing his 11-foot, 120-pound killer boards. His hardwood boards were a weird craft—angular, veering off, wide-tailed, concave (like a small Hobie Cat), racing across the flat. In 1946 I made the first all-foam surfboard. World War II had brought new materials into play, and I got hold of a few pieces of high-density Dupont foam. I experimented with different techniques on 5-foot blanks and was finally successful with one layer of 4-ounce glass and polyester resin. That was the first time foam was ever directly glassed, nearly a decade before Dave Sweet and Hobie Alter started building their all-foam and glass boards, and three years before the Kivlin-Simmons foam-and-plywood boards. It all would have begun earlier, but I couldn't get any more of the foam.

In 1948 I built Robin Grigg one of the earliest of my series of modern girl boards, which were lighter than usual and had a blended deck-and-rail rocker. Robin was the best girl rider at Malibu that year. She was one of the first in the new era of young women riding modern boards at Malibu. A board builder is nothing without top riders riding his boards. I was lucky to get Robin then, when

For surfing, Malibu was my main turf. The standing island pullout became my trademark. I threw in an arch I had picked up in Hawai'i for good measure, all done with my arms over my head like a bullfighter. It was a dead-ringer copy of Buzzy Trent fighting my dog Duke at Muscle Beach. The "soul arch," as it came to be known, was a maneuver that many hotdoggers on the coast—Dewey Weber, Kemp Aaberg, Mickey Dora, Lance Carson—would pick up.

Joe Quigg had built me a board in the early '50s before I went to Hawai'i. It was balsa, about 8 feet long, and weighed 13 or 14 pounds. It was the first "short board" ever built in California (to my knowledge). Traditionally, the Hawaiians had surfed shorter boards, but they were planks—thinner, heavier, and flatter, and they couldn't be hotdogged. Joe's board was prerevolutionary. I loaned it to Mickey Muñoz for several weeks, and he became an instant hot surfer. Everybody raved about that board, but oddly enough, the shortness never caught on. Nearly twenty years would go by before the short-board era would begin in earnest.

The other part of my life was study. My mom's ultimatum kept me at the books for five years straight, and I gradually improved as a student. In high school my favorite subjects were math and zoology. My math teacher, Robert Crawford, used to say, "The world wants results, not excuses." I never forgot his advice. From Santa Monica High, I went on to junior college for two years and then to Stanford University in Palo Alto, California, where I majored in biology. At Stanford I took a course in ecology from Dr. Donald Abbott, whose emphasis was on marine ecosystems. We visited Hopkin's Marine Laboratory in Monterey to study tide pools and shallow-water marine life. John Steinbeck had written about Monterey in his classic book *Log from the Sea of Cortez*. It was about an adventure he and the famous marine biologist Edward Ricketts had when they took a small boat to the Gulf of California on a voyage of exploration and ocean adventure. Staring into my tide pool,

a lot of the old-timers still did not welcome girls out at the Point at Malibu.

Another old-timer's bugaboo was young kids getting too uppity out in the lineup. Here again, a couple of years later, I was lucky to get an order from Ricky Grigg. He was the first young surfer to get what I call a "modern-era" surfboard. It was the shortest, thinnest, and lightest surfboard at the time, about 8'6", all balsa with a blended rail rocker and a very clean, balanced look. Ricky turned into one of the hottest surfers, faster than anyone before him, and blew right through the child-surfer-acceptance thing. Ricky was a wild and happy kid, full of energy, who went right on out to joyfully tear apart the biggest waves at Rincon, seemingly unaware that there was any reason to choke or prove your manhood. By 1953, Ricky was the first young surfer to be the best— better than Matt Kivlin, Leslie Williams, or anyone else—freely zooming and gyrating around the faces in tight, looping sections in this new style of riding. I'm sure his shorter board allowed him to be so good, and it's interesting that none of the other guys went to smaller boards. One reason was that in those days, before wet suits, only your hands got wet with the bigger boards, but Ricky was getting wet all over and had to come in and warm up frequently.

By 1952, Dale Velzy and Hap Jacobs opened their first shop at Hermosa and began pumping out short, light boards for the masses of young kids up and down the strand in South

it took on a larger significance as I fantasized about exploring the whole ocean. What I was dreaming about was being an oceanographer.

Surfing kept pulling me in another direction, even though it was toward the ocean. At Stanford, I would drive down to the coastal town of Santa Cruz almost every weekend and stay with my friend Peter Cole. Together we began to ride fairly big waves at Steamer Lane. The cold water (around 50 degrees Fahrenheit) and stormy conditions couldn't have been a better training ground to steel us for even bigger surf. By the time I finished college, I was ready to tackle the North Shore in Hawai'i—at that time, the largest known rideable waves in the world. I traded my college degree to my mother for my freedom, and in September 1958 I left California for Hawai'i to begin my life in the Islands. That was the year a small group of California haole began an assault on the huge North Shore surf. It was the beginning of a whole new era of big-wave riding. Oceanography would have to wait.

Bay. Velzy called them his "gremmies." By the late 1950s, John Severson was transforming the sport with his mod surf art, surf movies, and Surfer *magazine. John didn't write like a university textbook—he made it fun. He took the new, playful, youthful thing we had started at Malibu and introduced it to the world, never to return to the old-style boards or the old-style riding or the old attitudes about surfing. We all owe Severson.*

Matt Kivlin (inside), Joe Quigg (middle), and me at Malibu, circa 1951. Photo by Don Bane, courtesy of Joe Quigg.

Woody Brown, George Downing, and Buzzy Trent (left to right) slide a big one at Mākaha in the early 1950s. Scoop Suzuki photo.

3 PIONEERING BIG SURF IN HAWAI'I

Come ride the waves, the surf is high,
and hear the story of the surfer's cry,
Slide out on the shoulder and finish the ride,
your heart's on fire and your soul's filled with pride,
Taste the salt, the singing spray,
know the price a surfer must pay.

Woody Brown, Mākaha, 1950

In the early 1950s, I was in my middle teens in California, just beginning to tempt big waves along the West Coast. Every winter we typically had waves 10 to 12 feet, and there was one incredible day I will never forget. On January 10, 1953, the surf went ballistic. Rincon at Santa Barbara was 15 to 18 feet, and Overhead at Ventura was even bigger. I recall that spectacular morning vividly. I woke up and looked out our second-story beach-house window in Santa Monica and saw giant, rolling waves half a mile out. The surf was breaking beyond the Santa Monica Pier by the breakwater, where it is about 25 feet deep. The waves must have been at least 15 to 20 feet high, surf twice as big as I had ever seen it. Before I got out of the shower, the phone was ringing off the hook. Charlie Reimers, Peter Cole, Buzzy Trent, Joe Quigg, Matt Kivlin—everyone was headed north for Santa Barbara to surf The Overhead and Rincon. That was the day I caught my first triple overhead wave. I also got pounded, squashed, rolled underwater, and terrified; by day's end, I felt like a drowned rat. Despite the wipeouts, from then on I was absolutely hooked on becoming a big-wave rider. Nothing I had ever experienced was so dramatic. The huge waves were as magnetic to me as they were beautiful. I was drawn to them. I never questioned going out in the water that day. It was huge and I was scared, but sliding down those watery silver faces at Rincon was pure joy. It was a fleeting emotion, and like an addiction it would be something I would have to recapture again and again, never getting quite enough. That day changed me forever. Big waves were in my blood.

The early pioneers of big-wave riding in Hawai'i felt the same way about giant surf. They were addicts. In the early 1950s, a small cult of Californians lived in a Quonset hut at Mākaha Beach on the northwest coast

29

When surfers in California saw this picture of Jim Fisher, taken at Mākaha in 1953, many began to dream about riding big waves in Hawai'i. Walt Hoffman photo.

of O'ahu. Their names are legendary: Buzzy Trent, Jim Fisher, Walter Hoffman, and Woody Brown, along with George Downing and Wally Froiseth and a few locals who grew up in Honolulu. Jim Fisher was a daredevil who gained fame during this era for riding giant combers and surviving horrible wipeouts. Buzzy Trent and George Downing, though, were the first to successfully tackle the really big waves, in the range of 25 feet plus. They were the first masters of Mākaha. Trent was known for his power and high trim. He would never back down if properly lined up for the take-off. Downing was smooth and stylish. He had impeccable judgment and seemed always to be in the right spot. George was known back then as the Desert Fox, named by Buzzy after Rommel, the famous German general in World War II in the North Africa theater of operations. Downing and Trent were the first true matadors of big surf. They perfected the equipment and the technique for big-wave riding. With help from Joe Quigg, they invented the first elephant-gun surfboard, a stiletto tear-drop machine shaped like a spear, which would hold in on giant watery faces up to 30 feet high. Downing invented a bailout off the back of his board, a rapid sinking maneuver that helped avoid the horrendous wipeout of not making 25- to 30-foot waves. Trent exhibited the willpower, stamina, and true grit to take the wipeouts head on. On land, he could hold his breath for minutes at a time. In big surf, he could survive two-wave hold-downs. By the time I reached Hawai'i, in 1958, Downing and Trent had paved the way for us to tackle even bigger surf on the North Shore of O'ahu.

North Shore surf had been ridden occasionally in the 1940s and early 1950s but never on a consistent basis and almost never when it was truly big. An exception was a December day in 1943 when Woody Brown and Dickie Cross went out at Sunset Beach. For several hours the surf continued to build, and in the late afternoon it broke loose. By then, Woody and Dickie were far offshore, paddling for the horizon. As the waves continued to build, they figured they had only one chance to get in, by paddling 3 miles down the coast to Waimea Bay. At Waimea, a deep channel runs through the middle of the bay. Even the biggest surf rarely broke in the channel. Woody and Dickie reached Waimea close to sunset. Both were exhausted and both were terrified. Dickie made the first attempt for shore, but his timing couldn't have been worse. As he rounded the point and entered Waimea channel, a 30-foot clean-up set closed the bay. Neither Dickie nor his board were ever seen again. Woody waited offshore until it was almost dark. He had no choice but to go for it. He too was pummeled on the way in but somehow managed to keep afloat and eventually washed up on the beach. Brown described himself as too weak to stand. As he crawled up the beach on his hands and knees a couple of Army guys raced down to help him. According to them, Dickie Cross had drowned. They had seen him coming in, "wrapped up in this huge wave, and then he was gone"—over the falls, swallowed up by the sea. The life-and-death saga of Woody Brown and Dickie Cross postponed a full-scale assault of surfing on the North Shore until the late 1950s.

By the winter of 1957 a small group of Californians, including Greg Noll, Pat Curren, Bing Copeland, Del Cannon, Mike Stang, and Mickey Muñoz, had migrated to the North Shore. Mākaha was getting crowded, and they figured with caution and training they could handle North Shore waves. A small clan of Hawaiians led by Henry Preece had set up a grass shack on the beach at Haleʻiwa and were surfing there on a regular basis. Surfing the North Shore was an idea whose time had come. One day, the California crew was watching Waimea Bay. It was just starting to break at 10 to 12 feet. Greg Noll was convinced it could be ridden, and before long he was leading the pack paddling out. When they got to the lineup, though, there was more talk than action. Everyone agreed it was much bigger than it had looked from the beach—maybe 15 feet or even bigger. There were lots of wipeouts that day. No one was riding a board designed for high speed. None of the boards had cords. No one knew anything about the currents, the bottom depths, or whether the surf was coming up or going down. A few great waves were ridden that day, one in particular by Mickey Muñoz. It was around 18 feet, and Mickey, who had been one of the shortest guys in high school, was suddenly 9 feet tall. That day Mickey made varsity.

The following year, 1958, the campaign to conquer the North Shore began in earnest. As luck would have it, it was my first year in the Islands. I had graduated from college and was on my surfing sabbatical. I was ready to ride anything—well, almost anything. My first day out was with Peter Cole, who also had just arrived from California. The rain and cold of northern California had gotten the best of him, and like me, the stories

Buzzy Trent in 1955 with his Joe Quigg "elephant gun," which is where the surfing term "gun" originated. It was 19 inches wide and 12 feet long, built for huge point break Mākaha. Joe Quigg photo.

of big surf in Hawaiʻi had fired his imagination. On that first day, Peter and I were out at Sunset, where it was 6 to 8 feet and about as big as I could handle. Late in the day, a few 10- to 12-foot, eye-popping sets came in. Later that winter Peter and I would surf 12-to-15-foot waves with impunity, putting in six to eight hours in the water. Peter once made nineteen swims for his board (no leashes) in one day, and I was right behind with seventeen. By the end of the year, we were in top shape.

About two dozen of us were surfing big North Shore on a regular basis that year. The most respected were Greg Noll, Pat Curren, Peter Cole, Kimo Hollinger, Henry Preece, Buzzy Trent, Jose Angel, Paul Gebauer, Joey Cabell, and George Downing, to name a few. We decided Waimea could be ridden up to 30 feet. Bigger than that, the bay starts to close out. The rip currents turn into rivers too strong to swim against. The only way to get to shore during close-out conditions is to swim in hugging the right side of the bay. Buzzy Trent used to say, "Stay in the whitewater—it's your lifeline to shore." If you drifted left toward the middle of the bay, a rip current tearing out to sea would greet you. In minutes it would transport you back outside the lineup on the far west corner of the bay. The only way to get in was another round trip, but this time hugging the whitewater.

Late one afternoon I was out with Pat Curren and Paul Gebauer when it was 20 to 25 feet, clean and sunny, with an offshore wind. It looked so pretty from the beach that even a bodysurfer had decided to swim out. This bodysurfer, however, was not your ordinary bodysurfer. It was Jim

Caldwell, one of the fastest college swimmers in the nation that year. As the late afternoon faded into sunset, I wasn't paying much attention to Jim. A huge set loomed on the horizon and it was to be my shore boat to the beach that day. Some minutes later, standing on the beach watching the sun sink into the ocean, we saw a tiny head bobbing in the rip, heading west, fast. Through the roar of the surf, we could hear his waning yell for help. Jim Caldwell was heading out to sea. Pat Curren and I looked at each other and instantaneously decided to go after him. The next forty-five minutes were hell, circling the bay once, twice, and then a third time, finally hugging the whitewater with Jim clinging to my board and me clinging to Jim. Somehow we all finally made it in and washed up on shore, completely drained. Jim Caldwell said he owed his life to us. Well, maybe—but what makes this story unique is what happened twenty-five years later. On a small wave at Waikīkī an eighteen-year-old, blond-headed gremmie almost cut me out. Suddenly, he was apologizing profusely. "I'm sorry, I'm sorry, I'm sorry," he said, "Jim Caldwell is my dad."

I guess it was Peter Cole who discovered that you can't catch waves over 30 feet. First, he was one of the only guys with enough guts to try. This was in the late 1950s, when Peter was in his prime. Back then, Peter took off on 25-foot waves without even thinking about it. That was before he wore contacts. It was also before leashes, although Peter still refuses to wear one. It was also before he lost sight in one eye after his board skegged him one day at Sunset Beach. Peter Cole discovered that you can't paddle fast enough to catch a 30-foot wave, at least not very often. Over the years, Peter has been lucky and has ridden a few that big, but only when he's been in exactly the right spot. Waves travel at a speed proportional to the depth of the water where they break. A 30-foot wave breaking at a depth equal to its height is traveling at more than 20 miles an hour. To catch a wave moving this fast before it breaks is very difficult. You have to be a fast paddler and you have to be in precisely the right spot. This helps explain why so few 30-foot waves have been ridden, not to mention the guts part.

Greg Noll is another guy who has tested the limits of riding the biggest wave from a paddling take-off. He is said to have ridden a wave well over 30 feet at Mākaha on December 4, 1969. That day brought the biggest surf in the history of surfing in the Pacific Ocean. Waimea Bay was reported to be 40 feet. Mākaha was 35 feet and Ka'ena Point was 50 feet. Three days later in California it was 20 feet in La Jolla. I caught a wave at least 20 feet high on December 7, 1969, off La Jolla Cove and rode 1/2 mile all the way to La Jolla Shores by the Marine Room. The storm that produced this swell had a wind fetch of 1,800 miles. The winds in the fetch were 65 knots, and it sat stationary in the North Pacific 1,000 miles northwest of Hawai'i for forty-eight hours (see chapter 8 for more on this storm). Property

Peter Cole in his prime on one of the biggest waves ridden in the 1960s. Peter is 6'4" tall. Bud Browne photos.

damage caused by high waves to homes on the North Shore exceeded $1.5 million. Only a couple of people went surfing in Hawai'i during the peak of the swell. Greg Noll tells me his giant wave at Mākaha was the telling moment in his big-wave riding career. It was perhaps 35 feet high, a quantum leap bigger than anything he had ever laid eyes on. In his mind, he knew this was it. Now or never. Thirty years of training had gone into the build-up for this moment, and he said to himself, "Now." And what he did made history—the biggest wave ever ridden up to that time. Though Greg kept surfing for many years after the '69 wave, it was his ascent to the mountaintop, his moment in time. The beast within him had been conquered.

The 1960s were the years when the North Shore surf pioneers completed their study. Outside Pipeline was one of the last places to be conquered. I remember surfing it for the very first time in 1963 with Greg Noll, Bob Pike, and Mike Hickey. I spotted for them high up on the shore while they struggled to get out through a lull. After they got out, I joined them, although it took me four tries to get past the shorebreak. I remember paddling out almost half a mile, where I met them in the lineup. Then we all looked at each other and asked, "How the hell do you get in?" That day Greg caught his famous Pipeline ride, filmed in slow motion by pioneer surf photographer, Bud Browne. Greg kept going and going and going, and the wave kept getting bigger and bigger and bigger. Finally, it catapulted him off the nose as his board reached a point where it couldn't go fast enough to keep up with the wave. We all tested the limits that day.

The Next Generation

As the 1960s gave way to the '70s, a new era of big-wave riding emerged. The pioneering years, when the challenge was simply "survival," gave way to more stylish big-wave surfing. New moves, such as radical bottom turns, clean S-turns, and some serious tube riding previously accomplished in surf only up to 12 feet, began to show up in 20-footers. This increase in maneuverability was made possible by breakthroughs in board construction and design, particularly with the advent of lighter boards. The invention of the thruster (three fins) gave surfers an enormous increase in maneuverability. The equipment was honed by such master shapers as Greg Noll, Dick Brewer, Randy Rarick, and Pat Rawson.

This second era of big-wave surfing lasted through the 1980s. The surfers who impressed me most were Jeff Hakman, Jock Sutherland, Eddie and Clyde Aikau, Nat Young, Mark Richards, Ian Cairns, Mike Doyle, Barry Kanaiaupuni, Gerry Lopez, Reno Abellira, and Shaun Tomson. They were more athletic than their big-wave forebears, representing the elite of tens of thousands compared to the several hundred

Surfer *magazine introduced Pipeline to the world in 1962 with this shot of me on the inside Pipe. Photo courtesy of* Surfer *magazine.*

34

Buzzy Trent at Waimea Bay, displaying the power and determination that made him famous. Dr. Don James photo.

RIDING WAIMEA
by Buzzy Trent

Waimea Bay is a testing ground for guts—you either have it or you don't. It takes a special kind of surfer and a special kind of board to ride this place well. When this spot gets giant, it's beautiful! Waves come rolling, tumbling, ripping, smashing! Without a doubt this is the steepest menacing big-wave take-off spot in the Islands. You experience a thrill and fear at the same time. When you're on that wave, it's a good feeling. You've got only one thing on your mind—you want to make it, you've got to make it! You hear that familiar crack and thunder, you feel the wet spray, you're surrounded by blue, you're part of that blue, you just power through hoping you'll make it. Hoping you won't get the axe, and then—if you make it, if you've made that wave—you get a wonderful feeling inside you. You've made a fantastic wave and you feel good. And then if you don't make it, if you didn't make that wave, you either come in and cuss to yourself or else you paddle back out again amidst those Ghenghis Kahns.

contenders in the pioneering era. Waimea Bay remained the capital of big-wave riding, with Mākaha taking over top billing only once or twice a decade when Waimea Bay was totally closed out and unrideable at 30 feet plus.

The 1990s ushered in a third era of big-wave surfing, with major new technology—jet skis, restyled guns, footstraps—and the exploitation of the outer reefs, such as Jaws on Maui. The third era also includes an ongoing search around the world to discover and conquer the ultimate rideable wave, what Mark Foo called "discovery of Destination X." (I describe the third era in more detail in chapter 17.)

While big-wave riding today has become high-tech, one aspect has not changed and probably never will—the fear element. Buzzy Trent said it best while talking about Waimea Bay in an interview in *Surfer* magazine in 1966.

No invention, no high technology, no future trick will ever take the place of guts. As Buzzy said, "You either have it, or you don't." Amen.

4 THE BEST OF THE FIRST

His life was gentle, and the elements
So mixed in him that Nature herself might stand up
And say to all the world, "This was a man!"

Shakespeare
JULIUS CAESAR

Having lived in Hawai'i during most of the early years of big-wave surfing, I recognize a few men as outstanding among the best of the first. All possess distinctly different talents, but what they share in common is rugged individualism. Looking back, I see them as completely comfortable with themselves. To say they were loners is to overlook their gregarious qualities, but to a man, they did things their way. Strong, sometimes stubborn, unique, unconcerned with group values, often alone but never lonely, these were men you respected for their power. Most were all-around watermen—swimmers, divers, paddlers, sailors. They rode huge waves because they were drawn to them naturally. And like my own obsession with surfing, they did it for love.

Duke Kahanamoku inspired us all. Nadine Kahanamoku photo used with the permission of the Outrigger Duke Kahanamoku Foundation and DPKL.

Buzzy Trent and George Downing

Buzzy and George were the original top guns. While in one sense they were rivals and occasionally clashed in the water, they were also the best of friends, motivating and inspiring each other. At Mākaha they were the first to tackle truly big surf. Bud Browne has some footage of Buzzy Trent in 1953 sliding so fast on what appears to be a 25-foot wave that his board left the water several times before he finally got the axe. Downing was the analyst; he had Mākaha so wired he knew every boil on the surface of the water, every lineup and every set of bearings, the depth of every reef, and he used his knowledge always to be in exactly the right place at the right time. In the winter of 1994, I was paddling out one morning and rounding the bowl when I looked up to see George's son Keone perfectly locked in an 18-foot barrel. He was completely calm and wore a smile on his face as tons of water curled over him. His position was so close to the edge that one slip would have sent him over the falls, possibly hitting bottom or drowning. With all the judgment and poise of his father, Keone screamed through the tunnel without so much as a drop of water wetting his hair.

Buzzy and George have always been intensely private people. Neither will agree to interviews. For Buzzy, no interview is necessary for me to tell his life story. I grew up virtually being his personal mascot. For George, however, there is more mystery.

Buzzy Trent was eight years my senior as I was growing up in Santa Monica. In high school he was an All-State fullback on the football team. In track he ran the 100-yard dash in 10.1 seconds. Buzzy began surfing in the mid-1940s, when he was in his teens. His board was a 10'6", double-fin, square-tail concave. It was a Bob Simmons' masterpiece of Styrofoam sandwiched between plywood. The nose consisted of a huge spoon so pronounced that you could have mixed a salad in it. It was on this board that I caught my first wave.

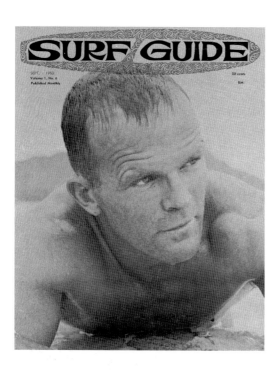

After high school, Buzzy went to USC on a full football scholarship. In his first year he got clipped and broke both legs. USC withdrew his scholarship, and the next thing Buzzy knew, he was out of college. He became a boxer in the Golden Gloves tournament, but again he met disaster. This time it was the other guy. He hit an opponent so hard it killed him right there in the ring. Next, Buzzy became a bullfighter in Tijuana, then a lifeguard in Santa Monica, and, finally, the master gladiator in big surf at Mākaha.

MY FIRST WAVE

I remember being nine or ten years old and body surfing at Malibu one day. Buzzy Trent was paddling his board back out to catch a wave. . . . As he passed me, he looked at me and said, "Hey kid, what ya doing?" And he paddled over to me and said, "You wanna catch a wave?" I said, "C-catch a wave?" "Well," he said, "come on," and he grabbed me by my arm and pulled me up on his board. I really still hadn't said anything—and he started paddling away. Next thing I knew, he started paddling for this wave. We started down and the board tilted up. I remember the tail lifting and lifting and lifting—and my eyes got wider and wider and wider. I was, by this time, just holding on for dear life—like an abalone clamped to a rock. And I could not—could not—let go of that board. Suddenly he stood up, and I felt his hands grasp my ribs. I was like a chicken who hadn't eaten in four weeks . . . just this tiny, shrimp-like human, clinging to this board, trying not to be ripped off of it. And he just scooped me up into his arms and planted me on that board. I was stuck there in this grip. We went screaming across this wave, so fast. The wave was curling; we were sliding . . . this blue water curling over us. I was terrified. And we kept going and going and pretty soon I started to relax. It was a long, long ride, and

Buzzy Trent on the cover of Surf Guide *magazine in 1963*

finally he let go of me. By that time I was just standing there, by myself. And the next thing I knew, I said, "Buzzy, how do we get out of this wave, cause we're coming to the beach." And there was no answer. I turned around and looked back and he was gone! He had fallen backwards and I'd been riding this wave by myself and didn't know it. And then I immediately fell off.

As told by the author to Jade Moon, in Ka Leo o Hawaii, *October 11, 1985*

Actually, with Buzzy you can't say "finally." After pioneering big-wave riding, he then became a hang-glider fanatic. He once jumped off the mountains above Mākaha during a kona storm and was blown 5,000 feet high. He almost froze to death before floating back to earth in Wahiawā, nearly 25 miles away. Buzzy ended his hang-gliding career by hitting a water tank going 50 miles an hour. He lost his kneecap on that one. Next he took up cycling, but no sooner had he begun than he had a serious head-on with a parked car. Later he was playing with his pit bull when it suddenly, for no apparent reason, bit him in the mouth and jaw and wouldn't let go. Buzzy had to strangle the dog to get it to release him. Buzzy says his pit bull is now in dog heaven. Today, at sixty-nine, Buzzy walks 20 miles a day, every day. You can see him on any day of the week, with hat and shades, head down, walking straight ahead along Kalani-ana'ole Highway, perhaps still dreaming of 25-foot waves at Mākaha.

Downing is more difficult to describe. He is an intense, intelligent, and proud man, with the best wave judgment of any surfer I've ever known. George has always been a guru at the beach, a natural-born leader. The beachboys consider him the ultimate authority on every subject connected with the water. No matter what the topic, if it's on the ocean—sharks, pollution, currents, sand erosion, you name it—George has an expert opinion and wants you to agree with it. And though I can't always do that, I have tremendous respect for his intuition and his experience in the sea. At Point Surf, Mākaha, there is no one I'd rather surf with. Along with Buzzy, George Downing was the greatest of the first during the 1950s. The North Shore pioneers all followed their lead.

On a 15-foot peak at Sunset, Downing displays his trademark form—notice the arm.

George Downing, master of style. Leroy Grannis photos.

Peter Cole

Peter Cole is the most stoked surfer I have ever known. At sixty-nine he is still in the lineup at Sunset Beach. If there is surf, no matter what the conditions, he will be there. I can remember dozens and dozens of times when the wind was howling sideshore or even onshore, and no one was out at Sunset, and Peter would say, "That can be surfed." Sure enough, out he'd go. Peter's strategy has always been to catch the biggest wave. While I was busy chasing down anything that moved he was patiently waiting outside for that one super set. I always felt you had to get your muscles warm and your body tuned before you could turn on and be on top of the sport. But not Peter—he only had eyes for the big one. He would wait with the patience of Job for the biggest wave of the day. And when it came, it was usually Peter Cole or Pat Curren who caught it. Once in a while, Greg Noll or Jose Angel or I would get lucky and one of us would score the biggest wave, but that was the exception, not the rule.

Swimming power was another advantage Peter Cole had over everyone else in the lineup back then. In college, Peter had been All-American and only missed making the U.S. Olympic Team by a fraction of a second. Peter could survive any wipeout, any hold-down, any swim. He was extraordinarily tough in the water. Given the forty years that he has put into the lineup at Waimea Bay, he must have ridden more big ones than anyone else, including all the modern guys. Today, when Peter paddles out at Sunset Beach, everyone cheers. He truly is the oldest and grandest man on the North Shore.

Peter Cole, still a stoked surfer. Sylvain Cazenave photo.

Peter's 6'4" frame doesn't hide the size of this Waimea giant. Steve Wilkings photo.

Jose Angel

Jose had no fear of big surf. He lived on the beach at Pipeline, and when the surf came up, it seemed to energize him, pulsing through his veins. At night, while he was sleeping, the pounding roar of wild waves seemed like an electric current charging his batteries, and when he woke up in the morning, there was no stopping him. Jose would paddle out at Waimea and take off on anything. Left of the peak, sometimes too soon (under the falls), sometimes too late (over the falls), but always in a supercritical position. He seemed to revel in surviving the most horrible wipeout possible. Jose even trained for a time to challenge 30–40 foot waves at Ka'ena Point. I called him Iron Man. When I surfed with Jose, I never worried about drowning because I figured he would somehow be there to save me. Over the years, we rode hundreds of days together at the Bay and at Sunset.

Jose and I were also avid divers and became black-coral diving partners for several years in the mid-1970s. As with surfing, there was no stopping Jose when he was diving for black coral. We had to dive to 200 feet most of the time, and with single tanks and decompression requirements, that gave us only about nine to ten minutes on the bottom. Jose was almost always at or slightly over the limit, many times exceeding it by several minutes. He got huge black-coral trees, but he also got the bends three or four times. We sold the black coral for jewelry—to Maui Divers or Shinkawa Jewelry. The stakes were high and the prize almost worth it.

One day in 1976, in Lahaina, Maui, Jose wanted me to dive with him on

Jose Angel was the first surfer to ride giant Back Door at the Banzai Pipeline, circa 1965. Leroy Grannis photo.

41

a new reef that he had discovered at a depth of 250 feet. He said it was virgin, with 25- to 50-pound trees (worth $500 to $1,000 each) all over the place. As tempted as I was, I told Jose that 250 feet was simply too deep for me. I would go with him, but not to dive.

That day proved to be tragic. Jose lost his life. He misread the depth sounder on his boat and he dropped into 350 feet of water. It was customary to use a 20-pound weight to get to the bottom quickly, and what probably happened was that Jose never looked at the depth gauge on his wrist. He simply went down at high speed, clearing his ears every few seconds but otherwise just relaxed. He probably sank deeper and deeper until he saw the bottom, but by then it would have been too late. He would not have known the depth, because his wrist depth gauge registered only to 250 feet. Most divers pass out from nitrogen narcosis at about 250 feet or, at most, 300 feet. The bottom where Jose dived was 350 feet. He never came up and there was no way I could go down after him. The current that day was running at 2 to 3 knots. It would have been impossible even to find his body. To descend to 350 feet in search of Jose would have been like jumping off a ten-story building. Had it been me on the bottom, Jose could not have gone after me, either.

Jose lived every day to the max. That day he had a smile on his face as beautiful as the rainbows over the West Maui mountains. He passed into the deep doing what he loved most, totally immersed in his element. I've never gotten over the despair of his loss, but I know he is at peace. Memories of Jose still inspire us all.

Pat Curren

Pat Curren has always been a man of few words. His motto was not to talk about it but just do it. And what he did was ride the biggest waves. He experimented with boards, perfecting Downing's guns, and his own, for the bigger, bumpier faces of Waimea Bay and Sunset Beach. Many of us in the original crew used his boards. Board builder Dick Brewer picked up where Pat Curren left off. Pat was a leader in other ways, too. He always sat at the head of the Viking table when dinner was served in his Quonset hut. He pounded on the table and uttered monosyllabic cries: "Food! Beer! Women!" But alas, there were no women. Several seasons came and went, and one day Pat did find a woman. Her name was Jeanine. Petite, quiet, and lovely, she seemed to exert a magical control over Pat. They were married and had a son, Tom. Twenty-five years later Tom was the best surfer in the world.

SURFER POLL
THE BEST SURFERS IN THE WORLD

1. Phil Edwards
2. Rick Grigg
3. Paul Strauch
4. Bernard Farrelly
5. Butch Van Artsdalen
6. Mickey Munoz
7. Greg Noll
8. Dewey Weber
9. John Peck
10. Joey Cabell
11. Pat Curren
12. John Richards
13. Mike Doyle
14. Mickey Dora
15. Lance Carson
16. Buzzy Trent
17. Donald Takayama
18. Hobie Alter
19. Corky Carroll
20. Rick Irons

The big-wave riders fared well in the first Surfer Poll, taken in 1964.

Greg Noll

We called Greg "The Bull," and no one has ever been more appropriately named. The name came from Greg's stance on his board. He was like a Sherman tank; once he was on his feet, there was no moving him. The Bull could plow through tons of whitewater without so much as a wobble. Knocking him off was like overturning a rhino. But it had not always been like that. Greg and I grew up together in Los Angeles Bay, Greg in Manhattan Beach and me in Santa Monica. Greg was tall and skinny and had arms as long as a chimpanzee. In paddling races, he was really tough to beat; pumping up and down from a kneeling position on the board, he was like an oil well, never tiring, as relentless as he was confident. Greg was a super hotdog surfer. His back turn was snappy, he hung ten, and he was the man on wheels before Dewey Weber. But then Greg began to grow, and he became heavier and thicker and stronger. During his years pioneering the North Shore, he was a force to be reckoned with. We all respected his power. Knowing he was in the water somehow helped us overcome our own fear.

Henry Preece, Greg Noll, and Buff. Leroy Grannis photo.

Greg went from the big waves on the North Shore to big-time fishing in the Pacific Northwest. He ran a shrimp trawler for years out of Crescent City, California. In the 1980s and '90s, he returned to surfing, but as an entrepreneur. He revived the spirit of the sixties—the boards, the woodies, the music, and the "two chicks for every guy" attitude. During the 1960s, Greg was one of the premier board shapers. He also produced several classic surf movies during this period. His book *The Bull: Life Over the Edge* was an enormous success. It put him back in the limelight, where he still shines today. Perhaps more than anyone else, Greg Noll has helped to glorify and institutionalize the pioneering years of surfing big waves in Hawai'i, and with that he has embellished the culture of surfing. When all is said and done, Greg Noll is one guy who lived up to his name, and that's no bull.

Greg Noll, Outside Pipeline, November 1964. The wave grew from 20 feet at takeoff to 25 feet. Photo courtesy of Greg Noll.

Paul Gebauer

Paul Gebauer was a charmer. He was extremely intelligent and talented. Paul played flamenco guitar like no other normal person around—like a protégé of Carlos Mantoya. And his surfing was like his music: romantic, with style and grace. Paul and I tried to apply this philosophy to big-wave surfing. In those early days, the style in vogue was basically stand up and go. Not much thought or effort went into performing in big waves. By contrast, in small surf, high performance was the in thing. Probably the two best and most graceful hotdog surfers in the world in the early 1960s were Phil Edwards in California and Paul Strauch in Hawai'i. Gebauer and I tried to take the tricks of Edwards and Strauch and apply them to big waves. We tried to accomplish small-wave hotdogging at Waimea and Sunset. We tried radical S-turns, cutbacks, bottom turns, and tube riding. Our boards were smaller (9'6" versus 10'6") and lighter (20 versus 25 pounds) than what most other guys in the water had back then. We took countless wipeouts, but we had great fun. As time passed, Paul became more and more absorbed in his music, in soul searching, in psychedelic experiences, and in drugs. He eventually stopped surfing, moved to Maui, and lived in the forest above Olinda, up-country on Haleakalā. I used to see him from time to time over the years, but I couldn't understand where he had gone. He seemed to have joined Jose Angel in a dive to infinity.

Joey Cabell

Joey Cabell is a jack-of-all-trades, yet he is uniquely Joey. From surfing to sailing, to diving, to skiing, to snowboarding, to windsurfing—Joey has done it all. And he has done it one better than anyone else. The man is a perfectionist. Every detail is scrutinized. When Joey commits to a sport, his intensity to excel is relentless. When you combine Joey's drive with his natural athletic ability and grace, you have an automatic winner. When I first arrived in Hawai'i, at age sixteen, Joey Cabell was already at the top, albeit in small Waikīkī waves. His acrobatics at Queen's and Canoes are legendary: standing-island pullouts, ten-toe hangtime, scooter boardwork, radical turns, and all of it so consistent that it seemed routinely mechanical. It was a repertoire way ahead of its time. In the years that followed, Joey gradually applied these skills to bigger and bigger waves. His proving ground in big surf was at Mākaha, reviving the tradition of George and Buzzy. The North Shore never had the appeal for Joey that it did for the rest of us. It was too windy, bumpy, and gnarly, and too crowded. Joey was a loner and he was into perfection. The glassy, crystal-clear, blue water at Mākaha provided for long, picture-perfect walls—not always as big as the North Shore, but clean.

Joey Cabell at the 1969 Duke contest. He won the event hands down. Leroy Grannis photo.

Along the way during the 1960s, Joey won more surfing contests around the world than any other surfer. At the same time, he was also into skiing, running his Chart House restaurant, and other esoteric adventures. He was always a man of mystery. After retiring from the contest scene, he built a chaletlike house on Kauaʻi, where he concentrated on riding Hanalei Bay bigger and better than anyone in history. The locals on Kauaʻi recall 20-foot days at Hanalei when the only guy charging was Joey Cabell, sliding at max speed with precision and control, totally dominating the session. Joey developed a speed stance, with his feet close together, and with it he carved turns on the face of the wave like shredding butter.

Much of what Joey did was away from the crowd, mainly alone. Many of his feats, especially in big surf, were not recorded on film. Joey wasn't doing it for the cameras. It was something emotionally deeper, very private, something between Joey and the sea. Like me, his romance was with the ocean.

Fred Hemmings

The last of the early pioneers of surfing in Hawaiʻi to whom I would like to pay tribute is Fred Hemmings. Fred was almost a generation behind the "best of the first." When Peter Cole, Fred Van Dyke, and I were schoolteachers at Punahou School, Fred was a student in the Junior

Fred Hemmings at Mākaha, where he won more contests than any other surfer. Photo courtesy of Fred Hemmings.

School in the seventh grade. Even then, Fred was a fantastic athlete. In the early 1960s, Fred won the junior men's surfing contest at Mākaha twice and repeated as senior men's champion in 1964 and again in 1966. By the late '60s, Fred was into big surf. He scored third place behind Mike Doyle and me in the '67 Duke in 18-foot surf, and the following year he won the first World Championship in Puerto Rico, in 10- to 12-foot surf. Fred is one of Hawai'i's all-time great surfers. But perhaps his greatest contribution to the sport of surfing was the creation of an international professional surfing organization, which he founded and served as president from 1976 to 1983. Fred initiated the first world circuit and the contests that make up Hawai'i's Triple Crown of surfing, the most prestigious series of surfing events in the world to this day.

In the 1980s, Fred moved beyond surfing into Hawai'i politics, where he served as a representative in the State Legislature for eight years. In 1990, he ran for governor of the State of Hawai'i, losing narrowly to John Waihe'e in a tightly fought race. Today, Fred is a statesman, a businessman, and an ambassador for the sport of surfing. He reminds us that great surfers can do more for their sport than just ride waves. Fred still surfs today when the big ones roll in at Mākaha and First Break in Waikīkī. And when kids paddle up and tell him, "You should have been here an hour ago," Fred retorts, "You should have been here thirty years ago."

Personal Impressions

And what about my own place in the sport of surfing during those early years of pioneering big surf? It always is difficult to talk or write about yourself; the risk, of course, is appearing egotistical. Fred Van Dyke and others have already accused me of this, though, so I suppose I have nothing to lose. Fred used to say that all big-wave riders were latent homosexuals. I think Fred was dealing with his deep-seated fears—he seemed to be challenging big waves to prove himself. Peter Cole used to say that Fred Van Dyke had more guts than all of us put together because of his fear of drowning, but he still went out in big surf.

Like Fred, I too was afraid, but perhaps not as much. I was drawn to big waves the same way I was attracted to beautiful women: Their beauty and power was something I wanted to be part of. My fear was something I simply dealt with. When I had to choose whether to take off on a 25- or 30-foot wave, it was always a tug-of-war between my lust for the thrill and a reasoning power in my brain that said, "Don't kill yourself for one wave." As I grow older, the reasoning voice in my brain gets stronger, and I find myself choosing smaller and smaller waves. When I was twenty-five, it was mainly adrenaline doing the talking.

Psychology aside, my thing in surfing was hotdogging. In surf lingo, this means acrobatic or high-performance surfing. It is typically how the sport is practiced today in all sizes of surf. In the 1950s and '60s, however, hotdogging was limited almost exclusively to small waves. My goal was to tame the wild thing, to cross the size barrier by taking hotdogging into big waves—and to do it "in control."

Today, I watch the big-wave hotdoggers of the 1990s carving circles around anything I might have attempted. Surfing has become highly competitive. The best surfers are the cream of a crop of millions. Their equipment is highly refined. The tow-in guys have jet skis to launch them into 30-foot faces. They fly across them with the grace of a ballerina and the power of a world-class athlete. I envy their ability and sometimes wish I could be out there in that groove. Duke Kahanamoku probably felt the same way about us back in 1967.

My career as a big-wave surfer did not last particularly long. For about ten years, I was in the magazines, the movies, and the endorsements (I did ads for Jantzen, Hobie, Dewar's Scotch, Greg Noll Surfboards, and a few others). My focus gradually shifted to the ocean at large: diving, adventure, and science. But before returning to school to study oceanography, I would travel to Tahiti to fulfill my childhood fantasy with *Drums of Pago Pago* and the romance of the South Seas.

RECOLLECTIONS OF RICKY GRIGG
by Peter Cole

Ricky and I surfed together almost every weekend during our years in Northern California at Steamer Lane in Santa Cruz. This was before we came to Hawai'i in 1958. In Hawai'i, I expected Ricky to attack a peak break like Sunset Beach with total confidence and ability as he had done at Santa Cruz. However, Ricky totally dominated the Sunset lineup those first few years on the North Shore, more than I anticipated. He was not satisfied with just riding the waves; he pushed the limits at the time by fading left, making bottom turns and turning up and down the face as had not been seen before. Sunset has always been both Ricky's and my favorite break and it has been fun surfing together all these years into relatively old age. I still see Ricky charging the peaks at Sunset as he did when we first surfed the North Shore. We are a little stiffer and slower getting up on the board, but the main thing is we are still having a ball as we both refuse to admit old age.

*Endorsements helped support
me through Scripps.*

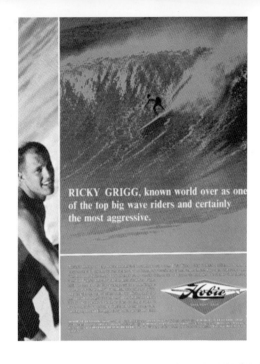

*Hobie boards pulled me
through many hairy
situations like this one.*

RICKY GRIGG, known world over as one
of the top big wave riders and certainly
the most aggressive.

*Dewer's gave me a case of scotch
for this ad, though I can't
remember ever drinking it.*

Fun and games. And
a little word play from
Jantzen. Great way to
keep the group in shape.

Jantzen spoken here.

*Corky and I enjoyed rubbing
shoulders with the big-time pros.*

DEWAR'S PROFILES
(Pronounced Do-ers "White Label")

RICK GRIGG

HOME: La Jolla, California

AGE: 32

PROFESSION: Marine Ecologist.

HOBBIES: Surfing champion, scuba diving,
photography, writing.

LAST BOOK READ: "Famine—1975."

LAST ACCOMPLISHMENT: Ph. D. thesis on
the population dynamics of marine organisms.

QUOTE: "People don't think you can pollute
oceans because they're so big. Well, the sky was
big too. Oceans will be used more and more for
food and I want to make sure they're used carefully. They're the last unspoiled resource we have."

PROFILE: Committed. Impatient. A realist, determined to apply his knowledge to today's problems.

SCOTCH: Dewar's "White Label."

BLENDED SCOTCH WHISKY · 86.8 PROOF · © SCHENLEY IMPORTS CO., N.Y., N.Y.

Dewar's never varies

Certain fine whiskies from the hills and glens of
Scotland are blended into every drop of Dewar's
"White Label."
Before blending, every one of these selected
whiskies is rested and matured in its own snug vat.
Then, one by one, they're brought together by
the skilled hand of the master blender of Perth.

Waimea Bay was the media's focus for big surf in the 1960s.

Sliding high and in trim, circa early 1960s. Bud Browne photo.

On the cover of Surfer magazine, 1961. Photo courtesy of Surfer magazine.

THE SURFER QUARTERLY

A John Severson Production

75¢

VOL. 2, NO. 3 - FALL

IN THIS ISSUE:
- THE AUSTRALIAN SURF
- MURPHY and the SURFING CONTEST
- SOUTH SWELL PICTORIAL
- BIG SURF PREVIEW . . Be Prepared

CALVALCADE OF SURF

y Bud Browne

Soul arching at Waimea Bay, on a surfing film poster by Bud Browne, 1963

5 TAHITI AND THE ROMANCE OF THE ISLANDS

Stories of the sea,
of the creatures who live in it,
of aborigines, and atolls,
of beautiful island girls
and lonely white wanderers
in search of Paradise.

Eugene Burdick
THE BLUE OF CAPRICORN

In the spring of 1959 my first season of big-wave riding in Hawai'i had come to a close. Despite having ridden waves at Waimea Bay, Sunset Beach, and Mākaha almost as big as they get, I was painfully aware of my shortcomings in equipment and surfing performance. It would be many more seasons before all of that changed significantly. By late February most of us who had committed to taking on these challenges were heading home to California or elsewhere for the summer to recharge for the next year. With college under my belt and my still-valid passport to freedom, my attention began wandering to places and dreams beyond Hawai'i. My fantasy with the South Seas and the romance of the islands continued to haunt me. I knew I must go to Tahiti.

Viewed from Tahiti, the island of Moorea, the Bali Hai of the Pacific, is stunningly beautiful.

Under Sail

In late February my adventure to the South Pacific began. I had been hanging around the Ala Wai Yacht Harbor in Waikīkī for a couple of weeks, hoping to find a yacht heading south. This was before an airport had been built in Papeete, when the only way to get to Tahiti was by yacht or seaplane. With virtually no money, for me the seaplane route was out. I would have to hire on a yacht as a deckhand and work for food and passage. Incredibly, only two weeks went by before I hit pay dirt.

The *Maunawanui* was smaller than what I had hoped for, but when the skipper, Athol Rusden, offered me the job as assistant cook, dishwasher, and deckhand, I was overjoyed to accept. On March 1, 1959, about one month before my twenty-first birthday, we sailed out of Honolulu. It was my first oceangoing voyage, and I knew absolutely nothing about sailing, life aboard a tiny yacht, or anything at all about the possible perils that might await us over the next 2,000 miles. As we rounded Diamond Head and set a course south-southeast, I wondered whether we would make it to Tahiti.

The *Maunawanui* was a 48-foot New Zealand ketch, and with eight people aboard, there was little space to call your own. I was assigned a bunk in the forepeak, the most forward hold in the boat, where the planking comes together to form the bow. My cabinmate was Unga Koloma-tangi, a taciturn Tongan, built of solid muscle and bone, who never smiled. He was going home by way of the Society Islands. In contrast to Unga, Athol never stopped talking and joking. When Ann Brisbin, the cook, and I served up dinner every night, he would always say, "I'm so hungry I could eat a horse and chase the rider," and he laughed no matter how many times we had heard it before. The rest of the crew were a mixed lot. Bill Parks, a doctor fresh out of medical school, was escaping the life his parents had chosen for him. Jack Ward was an anthropologist on a quest to figure out how the Tahitians managed to be so happy. Sybil and Ian Johnson were an aging couple in their seventies, and having worked diligently for forty years in Auckland, New Zealand, with little adventure in their lives until then, the *Maunawanui* was their last chance.

The first ten days at sea were horrible. I was seasick every day and must have lost at least 10 pounds. Sleeping next to Unga's sweaty body in the cramped forepeak was hot and smelly. The tradewinds never let up, and the constant pounding from heading directly into seas 12 to 15 feet high and sometimes higher kept opening up cracks in the forepeak hatch, allowing water to trickle in. My bunk was as damp and dank as Unga's back. I recalled the words of Dostoyevsky: "You build your character on the debris of your despair." My character was indeed building.

Our trip to Tahiti was anything but uneventful. Early one morning, about four o'clock, while I was on watch 700 miles south of the Big Island, the smell of smoke roused me from a semiconscious stupor. I shook my head and rubbed my eyes. Smoke was pouring through the floorboards from the engine room below.

Diary Entry, March 5, 1959

I quickly lifted the floorboards and was immediately engulfed in smoke. Running aft down the steps to Athol's stateroom, I pounded on his door and hollered for him to get up. In an instant he responded. Seconds later he was fumbling with one of the fire extinguishers on board but the goddamned thing wouldn't work. To our relief, Jack Ward had heard the commotion and rushed to our aid with the other one. Whoosh, and in three seconds the fire was out. A minute or two more and the fuel tanks would have blown. Too damn close for me. I was really scared.

The crew of the Mauna-wanui *(left to right): Rick Grigg, Athol Rusden, Unga Kolomatangi, Ann Brisbin, and Bill Parks (missing, Ian and Sybil Johnson and Jack Ward)*

A gas line had cracked and diesel fuel had been leaking into the hold. A flywheel spark apparently had ignited the fuel. After that I never again dozed on watch.

The days went by as though time had altogether stopped. The air became noticeably warmer and softer as we sailed farther south, and the winds abated. The sunsets were the reddest I had ever seen. Paradise felt closer every day. But before that, we would have to survive new and unexpected perils. One was running out of fresh water. The fire had burst one of the water lines, and we had to chase squalls every day to catch the rain.

The Atolls

After almost two weeks at sea we finally reached Caroline Atoll, and the coconut palms never looked better. Athol assigned Unga and me the task of going ashore to collect coconuts. Unga climbed the trees with a cord tied to his ankles, his feet and hands alternating to grip the rippled trunks. He scrambled straight up 40- to 50-foot trees. As I watched him rip off the coconuts and gleefully drop them, for the first time I saw him smile. My job was to carry all the coconuts back to our dingy. Unga shouted from the trees and razzed me incessantly for being weak and not carrying more coconuts per trip. Later that day, scheming to even the score, I challenged Unga to a spear-fishing contest. The reef was loaded with fish and gray reef sharks. The scent of blood in the water excited the sharks, and as they passed closer and closer, I could see Unga was becoming anxious. A shark about 6 feet long, a particularly pesky one, repeatedly dive-bombed Unga, perhaps because of his strong body odor. I saw my chance as the shark barely grazed Unga's head and veered directly toward me. I let go with my Hawaiian sling and speared it right in the eye. The last we saw of that shark, it was spinning out of control and heading into the deep. After that, Unga finally stopped giving me a hard time.

The tradewinds during the first two weeks of the trip had drawn us considerably eastward, off a straight-line course to Tahiti. As a result, our course took us directly through the Tuamotu Islands. The Tuamotus are atolls, islands built entirely of coral. In 1836, Charles Darwin had sailed here on the *Beagle,* and during his voyage he developed a theory to explain their origin. Given the circular outline of the atolls and their internal lagoon, Darwin reasoned they had grown up from the flanks of volcanoes that had long ago sunk below sea level. Years later my research as an oceanographer would help confirm Darwin's theory.

The next island we sighted was Mataiva Atoll. Like Caroline Atoll, it was an island only a few feet above sea level, and was visible only because of the coconut palms growing on it. We had been drinking coconut milk for three or four days, and its laxative effect had not helped me or anyone else regain the weight we had lost earlier in the trip. It was time to stop again and try and find some water. We made landfall late in the afternoon and secured anchor as the sun was setting. Athol had given Bill Parks and me permission to say hello to the natives and to try and get some water. Bill and I set out for shore in the dinghy. A small village was perched on the edge of the pass leading into the lagoon. As we gingerly rowed ashore, we were hoping the natives would be friendly.

Nearing the edge of the reef, we saw a lone figure walking toward us. She was tall, dark, and beautiful. I blinked and wondered whether this trip was a recapitulation of Michener's *Tales of the South Pacific*. "Iorana, bien venu. My name is Mary Ann and welcome to Mataiva." My God, she even knew some words in English! With my broken French, Mary Ann's broken English, and Bill Parks' boyish laughter, it wasn't too difficult to communicate. After twenty-two days at sea, we gratefully accepted Mary Ann's invitation to join her family for dinner. It was a night we will never forget.

Diary Entry, March 17, 1959
Before dinner we had a shower, and Mary Ann's mother gave us fresh short pants to wear. We then sat around and conversed as best as we could. There was a grandmother and four or five young kids, between five and ten years old. For the most part, everyone just smiled and giggled; they really seemed to enjoy watching our pleasure at the dinner table. The dinner consisted of anana (banana) poi, chicken rice, coconut meat crushed to make milk, flour cakes, and raw fish—so very good.

After dinner we continued to talk story and trade our life histories. When I mentioned Santa Monica, Mary Ann's face lit up. "Jo and Ben," she said. "Do you know Jo and Ben?" On the living-room table sat a recent postcard from Jo and Ben. Several years earlier they had passed this way on their own South Seas adventure. As the evening wore on, our friendship grew. Chatting with Mary Ann's mother, I barely noticed when Bill and Mary Ann got up and went out for a walk. About thirty minutes later, as I stretched and decided it was about time to start back to the ketch, a scream suddenly broke the quiet of the night.

Excusing myself, I hurried outside to see what had happened. Bill was running full speed toward our dinghy. Hurrying to catch up, I jumped in just as he was casting off. A look of dismay had replaced his boyish grin. "Ricky," he said, "You won't believe this. Mary Ann is a man." In our hasty departure, we had forgotten to ask about the water.

Papeete

Our final three days at sea between Mataiva and Tahiti were pleasantly uneventful. When we sighted the Diadems, the two highest peaks of Tahiti, rising high above the horizon, anticipation began anew. We hoped the incident on Mataiva was an exception and not the rule; and yet, in the grander scheme of things, it was consistent with my ideal that romance is the purest form of truth.

Diary Entry, March 20, 1959
At 6:00 P.M. we pulled in to dock at Papeete. The customs guys checked our passports and then, enfin après beaucoup de jours dans le bateau, we were ashore in the fabled land of love and excitement. My first impression was that of a beautiful, quaint town, with people bumping up and down the street on scooters and bikes, the damp heat of the sweet air melting over their bodies as they appeared and then disappeared into the night. Everyone was busy but not in a hurry; lots of music, and many sparkling, curious, brown eyes looked us over as if to say, "Welcome." About 10:00 P.M. hearts and emotions began to mingle with the casual atmosphere in Quinn's Bar. My first night in Tahiti was spent with Flora and her sister, and all that I had imagined about Tahiti came true.

Tahiti in sight after twenty-one days at sea

Tahiti met my expectations. I found a three-bedroom house near the water at Christian's Beach (named after Fletcher Christian, the mate in *Mutiny on the Bounty*) and, with two other guys off a yacht from California, rented it for $66 a month. Dividing the rent by three came out to $22 a month—the same rent I had paid at Fromm's Rooms in Waikīkī in 1953.

Life in Papeete was a party every night. We danced at Quinn's Bar or Bar Lea until midnight and then piled into a truck and drove to a dance hall, Lafayette's, out in the country. Lafayette's stayed open until three o'clock in the morning, when all of us by then either had found the girl of our dreams or were too drunk to care. Obviously, this could not go on forever. As the weeks turned into one month and then two, I began to grow restless. Mom had sold my '54 Oldsmobile in Santa Monica and had sent me $400, but living at this pace, my cash would not hold out for too much longer. Also, I had met Tevahine Merriterangi.

Tevahine was a Tahitian dancer and full of fun and love. She was totally "natural." For her, all things flowed from impulses and physical needs. I admired her for her carefree attitude and assumed it myself for most of my time in Tahiti. But other emotions were telling me that life was meant to be more than this.

Tevahine's father, Tani, was a pearl diver, and many nights when she was out dancing, I sat and listened to his stories. Tani explained that the

Approaching the island of Tahiti in 1959—before the airport was built at Faaa, before Marlon Brando, before the filming of Mutiny on the Bounty.

key to harvesting pearl shell was rapid descents and rapid ascents. The oysters with pearls grew between 100 and 150 feet deep and to skin dive (this was before SCUBA in French Polynesia) that deep, you had to go down fast and come up fast. Only then would you have enough time on the bottom to pick an oyster or two. The trick to getting down fast was to submerge with a heavy rock. The rock was tied off to a line, but a tender on the boat paid out the line so fast it was possible to free fall through the water with the rock under your arm. After harvesting the shell, the diver could then pull himself back up the line, which was taut, having been tied off on the boat by the tender. With adequate rest between dives, and hyperventilation, a diver could go down about twenty-five times a day, which usually yielded a harvest of twenty-five to fifty oysters. About 2 percent contained pearls, so with luck, a diver could hope to find one pearl a day. Over the weeks that followed, Tani took me out in his canoe to tend his line and train. With his technique, it wasn't long before I was skin diving to 100 feet.

The pearl-diving experience raised a whole new set of questions for me. Given the Tahitian divers' rate of harvest, how long would the pearl shell last? What was their growth rate, their age at harvest, and the turn-over time of the beds? Were they destroying a Garden of Eden? I began to think about returning to school to pursue an advanced degree in marine biology. Only then would I begin to uncover the answers to these questions.

Paradise?

There were other troubling observations I made in Tahiti. One was the human wreckage that frequented the wharf daily. Americans and other foreigners who had been in paradise too long had turned into vagrants or

56

alcoholics, and many were diseased. They were broken men. Was I seeing a vision of my future self, obsessed but outwitted by the dream? This paradise existence of the senses seemed to spoil: one day a delicious fruit, the next day sour.

For a time, I worked for Sterling Hayden on his famous yacht *Wanderer*. We visited all the Society Islands under the wind, "les îsles sous le vent" as they are known in French Polynesia: Moorea, Raiatea, Huahine, Ta'aa, and Bora Bora. It was the high point of my life up to that time. Discovering these unspoiled pearls of life and land was an unforgettable privilege. The people were warm and graceful, soft and gentle, simple and happy, and undistracted from the basic pleasures of life.

Diary Entry, March 28, 1959

Today, Athol and a group of French friends and I sailed over to Moorea and stayed in Cook's Bay, which is supposed to be the most beautiful spot in the whole world. This is probably the warmest, most affectionate place on earth as far as plain natural beauty goes. Here the world floats by in a dream, an idyllic refuge unsurpassed in the imagination. The small village is surrounded by sheer, black mountains, majestic in stance, with a jungle of greenery crawling up their faces, all of which encloses you in a such an impressive way that you feel at home, passionately alive, and yet mellowed with a soothing sense of tranquility.

It was difficult not to get off the boat right there and spend the rest of my life strumming a guitar. But other emotions continued to tug at my heart. Surely there was more to life. Or maybe not? Perhaps it was wiser to settle for the simple, happy life that lay at our feet?

The human wreckage in Papeete, however, posed a mighty contradiction to this illusion of paradise. My curiosity about the pearl shells and the vast ocean continued to weigh on my mind. So did the notion of next year's winter surf in Hawai'i. I couldn't do that and continue living as I had been for the past several months. I had family and friends back home. Becoming a happy native was not so simple after all. The sun was beginning to set on my South Pacific fantasy. My dream had been fulfilled, and though paradise was real, I had learned that it is fleeting. I discovered my true calling in "the ocean of truth." Sir Isaac Newton once described it in a poem as "a vast ocean of truth waiting, undiscovered for me." It was as deep as it was mysterious and far away. My quest was to pursue its study. After a month sailing with Sterling Hayden, I decided to return to graduate school to work on an advanced degree in oceanography. The day would come when I would return to Tahiti and relive the dream.

6 MY YEARS STUDYING OCEANOGRAPHY

Oceanography is fun.

Professor Roger Revelle
Director, Scripps Institution
of Oceanography, 1964

I had always wanted to be an oceanographer. My high school senior class yearbook documents my wish for the future: "To be an oceanographer in Hawai'i." While this nebulous and far-fetched ambition luckily did come true, the road was far from easy. Growing up on the beach in Santa Monica, my life from the beginning had been connected to the sea. In those early years, I gradually developed a philosophy of a total ocean life. Two things pulled at me. First, there were the physical activities in the sea—surfing, diving, sailing, and the competition. Second, I had an intense curiosity about all aspects of how the ocean worked. What produced the surf? Where did it come from? Why was the ocean warm on one day and suddenly much colder the next? Where did all the stuff that washed up on the beach come from? Why did the sand move in and out, widening or narrowing the beach? All the life in the sea fascinated me. My interest in the ocean was both of body and mind, twofold but inseparable, dual but connected, an equilibrium between the physical and the mental.

Opposite page photo by Ron Church

Getting Serious

The physical aspect—being in the ocean—was as easy as it was fun. "Gone surfing" was a sign I would never stop hanging on my door. The challenge for me lay in the mental aspect of learning about the ocean. Was I smart enough to become a marine scientist? For many of my early years, my older sister Robin had assured me that I was an idiot. In fact, she enjoyed describing me to her friends as a cretin. I had no idea what a cretin was, but my grades in high school convinced me and most of my teachers that I was not cut out to be a serious student. Mrs. Stetzel, my high school English teacher, told me I would never get into college.

One teacher, however, seemed to hold a glimmer of hope in my potential. Mr. Silvernail taught zoology. When he asked me if I was interested in being his laboratory assistant, I was so surprised that I accepted without realizing how much work was involved. Setting up the lab every day, giving preparatory "lectures" to the students, grading exams—I would have to learn the subject. So much for surfing every afternoon after school. Again, to my surprise, I did not mind. I discovered that taking the first step in beginning something difficult is the hardest part. Once committed, the job took over and it made sure that I got it done. This insight helped me realize that with some hard work, perhaps I wasn't so dumb after all. Maybe my dream of becoming an oceanographer wasn't impossible.

But first there were many obstacles to overcome. Mrs. Stetzel had been partially right about college. Stanford turned down my application, and I ended up at Santa Monica City College (a junior college) for two years. It was a second chance to get serious, and I realized it would be now or never. I was seventeen years old and had already been surfing for eight years. I could give up a couple of years of surfing and maybe, just maybe, I could reach my goal of living a total ocean life. First, I had to pass calculus, physics, chemistry, and biology. My two years at SMCC were exactly what I needed. I lived at home and had a little time to surf, but mainly I busted my ass in school.

I was working weekends in Santa Monica as a lifeguard and was involved in all the related water sports—swimming, paddle-boarding, rowing, and lifesaving. Every morning before classes, I surfed or paddled in front of my house. My dog, Duke, was my constant companion, waiting patiently for me on the shore, barking during my early morning ocean workouts.

First Catalina Paddle-Board Race

The summer of 1955, the City and County of Manhattan Beach sponsored a paddle-board race from Catalina Island to the Manhattan Beach Pier. The course was 32.5 miles, the longest paddle-board race ever held anywhere in the world—much more difficult than a runner's marathon. Some people doubted it could be done. Publicity surrounding the event attracted fifteen entrants, mostly lifeguards from California, but also the best paddlers at the time from Hawai'i. Tom Zahn (the favorite), Bob Hogan, and Greg Noll topped the list of entries from California. Hawai'i's best, George Downing, had also entered the race. For three months before the race, I trained. Every morning Charlie Reimers and I paddled 10 miles, from the Santa Monica Pier to Topanga Canyon and back. Once a week we did Santa Monica to Malibu and back—18 miles.

The day before the race, all fifteen competitors left the mainland for Catalina, each on a chartered escort boat. As dawn broke the following morning, a heavy fog hung over the water. I remember nervously taking my place in the middle of the pack at the starting line. The night before had been practically sleepless for me, full of worry and anticipation. We all had been issued standard lifeguard stock boards more or less alike, no lighter than 44 pounds and no longer than 11 feet.

The first hour of the race was a scramble. All the hot guys went out fast, disappearing ahead into the gloom. My strategy was to maintain a steady pace of about 4 miles per hour. I had never been a sprinter, and with 32 miles to go, there was plenty of time to catch up. As the miles wore on, my strategy seemed to pay off as I began to pass one paddler after another. Because of the fog, however, I had no idea of what position I was in. My escort boat had a radio direction finder but maintained no communication with the other boats. Toward the halfway point, my mother, who was on the escort boat, started to worry that I was getting too tired. In contrast, my girlfriend, Pat Schaeffer, cheered me on. There I was, going for broke, with my mom urging me to quit and my girlfriend urging me to keep going. After three months' training, there was no way I was going to quit.

After a while, I stopped passing people and assumed everyone had spread out so much that we were all on slightly different courses. I was in a trance, my arms revolving endlessly, with my mind in neutral. After eight grueling hours of churning, stopping only once each hour for one minute to swallow hot honey, my boat captain informed me that I had about 2 miles to go. We had not seen anyone for more than thirty minutes, and I was relieved not to have to sprint to the finish. I was totally out of gas. As we approached the coast, Manhattan Pier slowly came into focus through the fog. The pier was lined with throngs of people. Next I saw the beach, which was crowded with what looked like ten thousand people, all screaming. I still didn't know what position I was in, but the roar of the crowd sounded terrific. For the last 50 yards, I was on a wave. By then the crowd was shouting and running down the beach. "Congratulations! You're the first across the finish line!" I could barely believe my ears. Considerable confusion developed, however, over who had actually won the race. Tom Zahn had come in ahead of me, but he had not followed the prescribed course and did not cross the official finish line. After several hours' discussion, Zahn was disqualified and I was declared the winner.

Winning the Catalina race gave me a great boost of confidence. It is in fact why I include this story in my chapter about studying oceanography. Surfing also gave me confidence. It was more than a sport, more than a physical release; it gave me greater purpose to study the ocean. It gave me

*Winning the Catalina
Race in* 1955

The winner's circle after the running of the Catalina Race (left to right): Charlie Reimers, Greg Noll, Tom Zahn, Rick Grigg, George Downing, and Bob Hogan

Tom Zahn and me being interviewed after the more than eight-hour crossing of the Catalina channel. It was perhaps the most exhausted moment—and definitely one of the happiest—in my life.

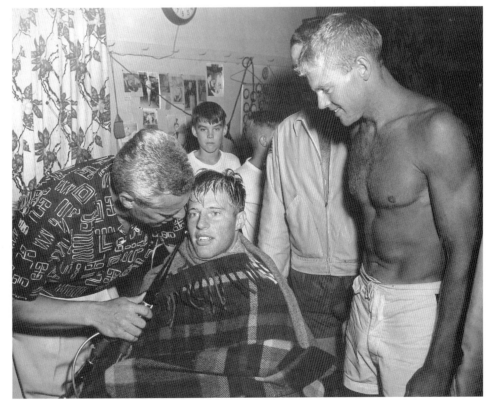

inner strength, an identity, and an insight into how everything worked. The dualism of a physical life in the ocean and a mental life studying it felt consistent, and right. The two activities blended into one. It was intuitive and natural, and ended up becoming my third rule of life: "Keep surfing."

University Years

From Santa Monica City College, I finally got into Stanford University. Some A's and a few good letters of recommendation made the difference. Stanford, too, was a confidence-builder for me; just being there was uplifting. Competing with the best brains in the country was occasionally discouraging, but it pressed me to my limits and then some; I learned how far I could reach. At Stanford I majored in biology. My professors were Dr. Page in botany, Dr. Geise in physiology, Dr. Myers in vertebrate evolution, Dr. Abbott in invertebrate zoology, Dr. Bonner in chemistry, and Dr. White in physics. Surfing had to take a back seat to my career, but not without weekends at Santa Cruz. After two years of intense study at Stanford, I graduated with a bachelor of science degree in June 1958.

My life study of the ocean, however, didn't begin in earnest until several years after graduation from Stanford. My plan was to take a year or two off and surf in Hawai'i. I had fulfilled my contract with my mother to finish college, so the road ahead was completely up to me. I am grateful now that I listened to her long enough to get through college. It gave me a solid foundation for planning the future. Nevertheless, my first priority then was to surf big waves in Hawai'i, and there was still that lingering romantic fantasy from my childhood—the lure of South Seas adventure. Perhaps I could begin my career in oceanography at the University of Hawai'i. The plan could accommodate both surfing and oceanography.

Three years went by before I returned to school. First there would be two seasons of riding giant surf and roving the South Seas. I was not absolutely positive about being a marine scientist, and the time would help me sort my priorities. In Tahiti I discovered that paradise was not all that it had been cracked up to be. After three months there, the idea of a more serious life made more sense. Tahiti had been a time of freedom and total abandon, but I could sense that a life of pleasure there could easily spoil. I decided to return to Hawai'i, first to work on a master's degree at the University of Hawai'i and then to apply to Scripps Institution of Oceanography back in California. And a couple more years of school in Hawai'i would allow more surfing on the North Shore between classes.

At the University of Hawai'i, I studied the ecology of black coral for my thesis dissertation. Black coral was used to make jewelry, not all that different from pearls. From the *Drums of Pago Pago* to my dives with Tani in Tahiti for pearl shell, black coral seemed to be the perfect subject

to study. It grew only in deep water, below 150 feet, and practically nothing was known about its ecology. I spent the next three years determining its depth range, growth rates, birth rates, and death rates. I calculated that 10,000 pounds of black coral could be harvested annually by Hawaiian fishermen without damaging the ecological balance of this precious resource. This information was important in establishing a management plan for the black coral fishery in Hawai'i. It also earned me a master's degree and an acceptance to pursue a Ph.D. at Scripps.

Scripps Institution of Oceanography

I entered Scripps Institution of Oceanography in the fall of 1964. Our class of thirty students, most with bachelor's degrees, had been selected from the best universities in the world. My application had been considered borderline, but because I already had a master's degree, they decided to give me a chance. It would be the six most difficult years of my life.

My first day at Scripps was memorable. All the new students had assembled for an initiation lecture in Sumner Auditorium, to be delivered by the director, Roger Revelle. Revelle was an immense human being, both physically and intellectually. He had put Scripps on the map during World War II and thereafter with ground-breaking research and discoveries. Now he was head of the largest oceanographic institution in the world, staffed by more than eight hundred scientists in ten research institutes or groups and supported by numerous laboratories, piers, and other research facilities, as well as eleven oceangoing ships. Roger Revelle climbed the podium steps to the lectern, smiled his broad smile, and began the invocation. His first words were "Oceanography is fun." Looking back today, after three decades of research and teaching, I couldn't agree more, though I would hasten to add that it is also a tremendous amount of hard work.

Scripps Institution of Oceanography was founded in 1903 by William E. Ritter, with generous support from E. W. Scripps and Ellen Browning Scripps. E. W. Scripps owned thirty newspapers across America and was said to be a recluse—a damned old crank, but nevertheless fascinated by natural history. His vision led SIO to affiliate with the University of California in 1912. My class of 1964 would mark its fifty-second year of marine research and education. As I sat in Sumner Auditorium listening to Roger Revelle, an extraordinary wave of inspiration swept over me.

I would have to put surfing on the back burner for a while to meet this new challenge. But this was easier said than done. There always seemed to be distractions: surfing contests, world tours with surf film companies, even requests to "act" in Hollywood movies.

Roger Revelle, director of the Scripps Institution of Oceanography from 1962 to 1966, demonstrating a radar beacon to several graduate students on their first voyage on an oceanographic ship.

WORLD PREMIERE

TUESDAY JULY 18th

KIPS BAY THEATER
2ND AVE. & 31ST ST.
Daily 1·3·5·7·9 SATURDAY 1·3·5·7·9·11

opening Week Special
·Meet In Person·
RICKY GRIGG·GREG NOLL

Surfing Goes Hollywood

In the 1960s the rapidly increasing popularity of surfing generated a new industry dedicated entirely to the media. Surfing magazines and movies captured the imagination of the young generation. Surf movies, in particular, glorified the visual delights of the sport and sent surfing shock waves across the country. It was a genre begun by dedicated 16-mm photographers who loved the surf and lived the sport.

The early surf films were classic, with a simple message: lots of surf, a carefree life, a little slapstick comedy, and the drama of killer waves. For a comedy scene, Greg Noll and I once rolled an old surf-wagon off a cliff near Ka'ena Point. Unbelievable and fun in those days—unthinkable and illegal today. The films typically were shown in high-school auditoriums, accompanied by live narration from the cinematographer and the intoxicating music of the day: the theme from *Peter Gunn,* Dick Dale and his Del Tones, or the Beach Boys. The most famous of the early surf cinematographers were Bud Browne, John Severson, and Bruce Brown. They each churned out yearly films, with such titles as *Surf Fever, Surf Surfari, Cat on a Hot Foam Board, Slippery When Wet, Big Wednesday, Cavalcade of Surf,* and *Spinning Boards.* These films fueled a craze that swept the surfing beach cities across the country. It was the era of Surf City, USA.

From the start, Hollywood responded to the commercial pulse of surfing and further promoted the mania with a series of beach-blanket bombs. The first was *Gidget,* produced in 1958, which glorified the sun-bleached surfing cult, the beach parties, and the mindless subculture of pure fun. Gidget, short for "girl midget," was a Malibu groupie who worshipped the boys at the beach, who were depicted as surf gods. *Gidget* introduced millions of people to surfing. In the early '60s, Columbia Pictures produced a triad of cornball clones: *Beach Party, Muscle Beach Party,* and *Beach Blanket Bingo.* The plots were unbearably thin, built around bikini contests, beach parties, and surfing contests—winner gets girl and a sunburn. "Hey man, but it was cool." It was America before it was time for that generation to get serious. It was post–Korea and pre–Viet Nam. There was a corny-but-wholesome innocence about these movies. As time passed, their quality deteriorated. *Ride the Wild Surf* was so contrived—with fake surf shots taken in a Hollywood pool—that even the teenyboppers groaned. *How to Stuff a Wild Bikini* (American International Pictures) topped it off with beach-bashing boys and their bikini beauties. A few surfers were making some money in Hollywood, and when Greg Noll and I starred in *Surfari,* in 1967, the surfing media hype was cresting. The market for mindless surf films was nearly saturated. When our movie opened at Kips Bay, in New York City, we enjoyed three or four nights of full houses, and after that it was all downhill.

Dropping down the face of a Banzai Pipeline heart-stopper—caught on film in a real surfing movie, Bud Browne's Spinning Boards.

Surfari *was my first and last role in a Hollywood movie. Tinseltown and my lousy acting saw to that.*

SEVERSON STUDIOS PRESENT

SURF SAFARI

NEW COLOR SURFRIDING MOVIE

SURF WITH

RICKEY GREGG · PETER COLE
MIKE DOYLE · DEE-O
SONNY VARDIMAN · PAT CURREN
TOM POWELL · TOM SWEENEY
PETER VAN DYKE · BOBBY
PATTERSON · BILL COLEMAN
JOSE ANGEL · MARGE PHILLIPS
BOB SHEPPARD · JOEY KABEL
MICKEY MUNOZ · CORKIE COLE
HI-HO SILVER · JACK HALEY
FRED VAN DYKE · MIKE KEELER
HENRY PREECE · KEN TILTON
KIMO HOLLENGER · SAM SHERMAN
GRANT ROHLOFF · JANE SMALL
AND A CAST OF THOUSANDS

DON'T MISS

GIANT REDONDO SURF
SURF BEACH SAFARI
YOKAHAMA BLASTERS
PT. CONCEPTION TUBES
SUNSET BEACH · MAKAHA
WAIKIKI · ALA MOANA
WAIMEA BAY · HALEIWA
SAN CLEMENTE · COTTON'S PT.
SAN ONOFRE AND MORE!

The spaghetti fight after the skateboard contest all but killed it. To the benefit of my career in oceanography, that fiasco ended my acting days.

Thirty years later, Hollywood today occasionally produces a movie with a surfing story-line, and though they have improved a bit, no Oscar pretense here. The real surf movies are still around, but that realm has changed, too. They probably reached their apex in the late 1960s with the 35-mm general release of Bruce Brown's best film, *Endless Summer,* which enjoyed tremendous success by capturing the pure stoke and freedom of surfing. Surf movies today seldom have a general release or tour the auditoriums or theaters, as they can be bought on video. TV covers the sport extensively. The heyday of homemade surf movies has passed, but it was fun to be part of the evolution of surf films. All of us who were there would say, "Cowabunga."

Surf Safari, produced by John Severson, starred all my pals and a cast of thousands.

Another "part" in Hollywood was teaching Yvette Mimieux to surf for an episode of the TV series "Dr. Kildare" written by my old friend Ben Masselink. One day Yvette drove down to La Jolla to do a shoot with me for the show. I had received permission from Scripps for the camera crew to film the scene from the Scripps pier. No sooner had Yvette and I entered the water than a crowd gathered. Yvette was supposed to catch a wave, stand up, and then go into an epileptic fit, tumbling out of control off the board. My job was to push her into the wave and then make sure she made it safely back to shore after the wipeout. Everything went as scripted until Yvette hit the water. *Pop*—off came her bikini top. The crowd on the pier erupted in cheers and applause. Unfortunately, that take ended up on the cutting-room floor.

Several days later my department chairman, Dr. John McGowan, called me into his office. McGowan warned me that I had best compete at Scripps, and Scripps alone, or my scholarship very likely would disappear. With several other boondoggle movies in the offing, I knew it was some of the best advice I would ever receive. The demands of graduate school meant I could not do both. I decided a Ph.D. was a more reliable ticket to freedom than a list of Hollywood credits. I would be able to go anywhere in the ocean, and I would be able to study the waves that I loved to ride. In Hollywood, I probably would have ended up beholden to the puppet strings of directors, producers, and people who did not understand or care about the ocean. I decided to redouble my efforts at Scripps.

After the first two years, with the core courses behind me, I began research on my dissertation. I focused on the ecology of temperate-water corals. For the next three years, I dove off La Jolla in the kelp beds three days a week to monitor their growth rates, birth rates, and death rates. I discovered that gorgonian (sea fan) corals had annual growth rings in their skeletons, like trees. Knowing the age of all individuals in the population, I could accurately determine their death rates, the way an insur-

ance actuary does for human beings. I also worked out their life history, which demonstrated how they survive long enough to reproduce. "Replacing yourself" is a rule of life that applies to all species. It was interesting to submerge my consciousness into the necessities of survival for another species. Like a window into the human soul, the corals showed me how their species and my own share the need to survive and reproduce.

Living and working at Scripps was intense. Surrounded by the genius of the faculty and meeting its standards of excellence was a source of constant pressure and ongoing inspiration. John Isaacs, one of the grand old men of science at Scripps, often dropped in at my office late in the day on his way home. One of his favorite sayings was, "Your reach should always exceed your grasp." It was the same philosophy and vision that inspired John F. Kennedy to put a man on the moon. The space program in fact, would have an impact on oceanography and my life during my years at Scripps.

In 1965, the United States' Man in the Sea program, headed by John Craven, launched *Sea Lab II.* Its purpose was to explore the ocean, the inner space of planet earth. Lyndon Johnson's Great Society had refocused part of our nation's space program back to earth. Scott Carpenter, the second man to orbit our planet, was chosen as the team leader for the project. I too applied and was chosen by the Navy to be one of thirty aquanauts to live underwater at 205 feet for fifteen days off Scripps. Four other diver-scientists from Scripps joined twenty-five Navy career divers to round out the team. (In the next chapter, I tell the full story of our adventure living at the bottom of the sea.)

Sealab II, like surfing, pushed me into the limelight at Scripps. Though most colleagues were supportive, a few regarded living under the sea as more stunt than serious science. *Sealab II* was indeed high profile, and some faculty members seemed to resent the program; graduate students were not supposed to upstage the faculty. I often thought that if they would only learn to surf, they might mellow out. It helped me remember my third rule of life, "Keep surfing."

I occasionally experienced another perplexing problem at Scripps. People commented on my dual pursuit of surfing and oceanography. These people were usually nonsurfers and nonscientists, and they seemed to express an admiration for my interest pursuing two careers. They wanted to know how I did it. Many people at Scripps, though, did not regard it as admirable. They seemed to resent the idea of a surfer in their midst. Similarly, some in the surfing community sometimes dismissed my surfing because I was a scientist. Both groups adhered to a pure-membership mentality. Half-timers were excluded. It seemed I had to do it one better to remove the serious doubts. Even today, after three decades as a research professor, some scientists do not take me seriously because I surf. Surfers are more tolerant, but I guess after a lifetime of riding waves you become a brother. I feel like two distinct people, leading a double life. It has not been an easy road to follow, but the dual lifestyle has been extremely rewarding.

My six years at Scripps meant missing lots of surf, but it was worth it. The 1960s were exciting years to be studying oceanography. For example, marine geology was undergoing a complete intellectual revolution. Sea-floor spreading had been discovered. The crust of the earth no longer was viewed as static. Instead, the sea floor was found to consist of mobile plates, constantly forming at the edges of ocean ridges and disappearing along their opposite sides by sinking back into the earth's mantle, a process known as *subduction*. By the 1970s, the earth's crust would be considered dynamic, constantly moving and undergoing formation and subduction. Alfred Wegener's theory of continental drift, first advanced in 1910, was confirmed.

It was an opportune time to enter oceanography. My Scripps class was on the cutting edge, exploring the frontiers of science. My specialty was biological oceanography, which includes everything from plankton to whales, barnacles to coral, bacteria to birds, the ecosystem and its stability, and the effects of pollution, global climate change, greenhouse gases, and El Niño.

The most valuable thing I learned at Scripps was not facts or theory but rather how to think critically; how to recognize bias; how to keep an open mind; how to weigh the best information against what people would like me to believe or wanted me to believe. Knowledge is power, and like truth, it sets you free. Ben Masselink summed it up at my graduation in 1970 when he assured me that a Ph.D. was a gift of learning that no one could ever take away.

Collecting plankton at sea from an oceanographic vessel

Sealab II *was officially christened in Long Beach, California, before submergence in August 1965 off La Jolla, at 205 feet.*

7 LIVING UNDER THE SEA IN SEALAB II

The Owl and the Pussy Cat went to sea
In a beautiful pea-green boat;
They took some honey, and plenty of money
Wrapped up in a five-pound note.

Edward Lear
THE OWL AND THE PUSSY-CAT

The idea of people living under the sea sounds like a Jules Verne science fiction adventure. Like Captain Nemo, who traveled 20,000 leagues under the sea in his mythical submarine *Nautilus,* to live underwater has always been the stuff of dreams. And like many young people growing up, I too had dreamed of living under the sea. I had imagined I could find treasure or discover something unknown like a giant squid or a shipwreck.

The Race for Inner Space

The U.S. Navy in the early 1960s took the idea of living undersea very seriously. When the U.S.S.R. launched *Sputnik,* the first satellite to orbit the earth, the United States responded energetically, not only in space research but also in science research and development in general. The Office of Naval Research organized the Man in the Sea program beginning in 1964, when four American aquanauts lived undersea at a depth of 192 feet for eleven days off Bermuda. The following year, *Sealab II* extended the U.S. capability to 205 feet for a mission that lasted forty-five days, this time for thirty men. It was my good fortune to be selected as one of the aquanauts.

In the early 1960s, France entered the race for access to the continental shelves of the world. These shallow shelves ring the continents, ranging up to several hundred miles wide. They are generally covered by 600 feet of water or less and comprise more than 10 million square miles, some rich in minerals, petroleum, and natural gas resources. The capability of humans to live and work at depths down to 600 feet represented a huge economic opportunity.

Under Jacques Cousteau's Conshelf Program, France first put two men in a habitat off Marseille at 35 feet for seven days in September 1962. The

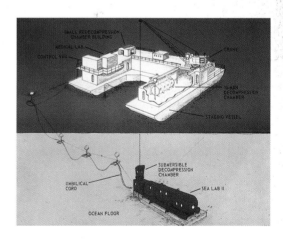

Sealab II was supported by two umbilical power cables, one from shore and the other from a supply barge anchored directly overhead.

73

Scott Carpenter, former astronaut, and our team leader in Sealab II

following summer, Cousteau's diver-scientists occupied *Conshelf II* in the Red Sea for seven days at 85 feet. In 1965, France and the United States both were pressing for deeper penetration of the continental shelves. *Sealab II* was installed at 205 feet off La Jolla, California, while the French jumped ahead to 330 feet with *Conshelf III* in the Mediterranean Sea.

The competition between the U.S. and French teams may have been intense, but we shared equally in the adventure. On October 1, 1965, a telephone link was established between *Sealab II* and *Conshelf III*. Separated by 8,000 miles and two oceans, the two teams conversed first in English and then in French; the strange mixture of exotic gases we were breathing (helium, nitrogen, and oxygen) made us all sound like Donald Duck. Because I could speak a little French, I was selected to pass along our congratulations to the French team. Over the phone, I read a carefully rehearsed paragraph, summoning my best French. After I finished speaking, André Leban, the French team captain, thanked me warmly for my comments, but added that he had some trouble understanding my English. I had ten days underwater with nine Navy divers to live that one down.

The primary mission of *Sealab II* (the "habitat") was to test humans' ability to live and work at significant depths on the continental shelf. The specific goals were threefold: to test human performance, to solve specific engineering problems, and to accomplish scientific research on the biology of mid-depth shelf ecosystems. Five science-divers were selected from Scripps to join the team of Navy divers. Our mission was to accomplish the third objective of the project—studying how the habitat would affect fish ecology and bottom communities in the immediate area where it was placed on the bottom.

What we discovered was remarkable. *Sealab II*—its physical structure,

SEALAB SPECIFICATIONS

The sealab was essentially a long, steel chamber, 12 by 57 feet, anchored to the bottom by a four-point mooring and its own weight of 45 tons. Resting on a set of pods several feet off the ocean bottom, the lab was equipped to house a team of ten aquanauts. The living quarters included ten bunks, two toilets, a hot shower, a kitchen and scientific lab area, plus a diving entry-exitway. Access in and out of the sealab was by way of a ladder through a 4-foot opening in the bottom of the habitat. Because the pressure inside the habitat was precisely equal to the pressure of the outside, the entryway in the bottom of the habitat could be left open without the water coming in. From inside, it was like walking down steps into a little pool. The skirted entry led directly into the open ocean. Each aquanaut made several dives to the surrounding environment each day. Anchored at a depth of 205 feet, the habitat was situated only 150 feet from a deep submarine canyon, which, in turn, dropped almost vertically another 400 feet. The canyon allowed sorties by the aquanauts to 300- or even 400-foot depths.

All power and communications were supplied by two umbilicals, one leading directly overhead to a surface support barge and the other to the mainland of La Jolla and the Scripps campus. We were in constant communication either with topside or the outside world. Four television cameras mounted at various angles

74

as well as the lights and sounds it produced—was like a huge magnet. An entire community of sealife formed, gradually increasing in abundance for about a month before leveling off for the last two weeks. While we were there the biomass of all species around the habitat increased almost one hundred times. We were enveloped by fish, swarming plankton, squid, sea lions, and other creatures. It was a fishbowl, but we were the ones on the inside looking out. *Sealab II* was an extraordinarily successful artificial reef.

Living on the Bottom of the Sea

Living in the sealab was a rigorous experience. Most of the aquanauts developed skin rashes or ear infections brought on by the near 100 percent humidity. In spite of carbon dioxide scrubbers to cleanse the air and dehumidifiers to reduce the humidity, the atmosphere was hostile. The first three days on the bottom, all of us experienced strange joint aches and periodic headaches. Those who were overweight became lethargic, while the thinner types became overactive. It seemed that the environment, both socially and physically, magnified personality traits, converting moderate to more extreme behavior. After about ten days, people were getting on each other's nerves. I remember thinking how ugly the wart looked on Shorty Wells' nose after two weeks on the bottom.

Other physical problems arose, some good and some bad. You could feel waves passing overhead on the surface by the change in pressure on your eardrums. I didn't mind, because it told me what the surf was doing. Others, though, complained that it added to their difficulty sleeping. Then there were scorpion fish, with venomous dorsal fins, surrounding the habitat. The lights had attracted so many scorpion fish in the entryway that it was difficult getting in and out without stepping on or brushing

inside the lab meant that we were being monitored twenty-four hours a day. The psychologists on the other end of the cameras regarded us as they would guinea pigs. A voice unscrambler normalized communications from the bottom; our voices were squeaky because of the exotic mixture of light gases we were breathing: 75 percent helium, 21.8 percent nitrogen, and 3.2 percent oxygen. At 205 feet, the pressure inside the habitat was equal to 6.2 atmospheres. This meant we could breathe only about 3.2 percent oxygen. The internal pressure of 6.2 atmospheres times 3.2 percent oxygen produced a partial pressure equivalent to about 20 percent oxygen (6.2×3.2) at the surface. A higher level of oxygen would have resulted in toxicity and convulsions. It was an interesting way to learn that oxygen is a poisonous gas at high concentration.

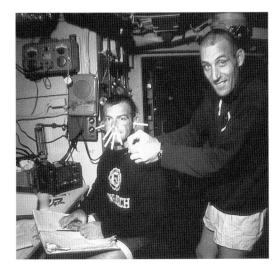

Bill Sheets and Shorty Wells suffering withdrawal symptoms after fourteen days living in Sealab II

Large aggregations of fish were attracted to the lights of Sealab II *night and day.*

against one. Scott Carpenter, our team commander, was severely stung on his hand and almost had to cut short his stay on the bottom. Scott was on loan to the Navy from NASA to head the training program for *Sealab II.* In 1962 he had been the third man in space and the second to orbit the earth in the Mercury Program. During our stay on the bottom, Scott received a call from President Lyndon Johnson congratulating him and the rest of the team on the success of our mission.

Looking back, what I remember most about *Sealab II* is the nights spent lying in my bunk peering outside through a 2-foot port into a sea of milling fish, plankton, and squid. It was a window that opened into a world of natural selection, survival; it was eat or be eaten. Occasionally, a sea lion dove down to forage on *Loligo* squid. We would watch as a sea lion bit a squid, which squirted clouds of black ink. A squid once gripped my port glass with its tentacles, trying to escape capture. The sea lion shook the squid violently, ripping it off the glass.

The Scripps ecology team of Art Flechsig, a research oceanographer, Tom Clarke, a fellow graduate student, and I occupied the sealab for fifteen days each, making our total period of observation forty-five days. We published an article describing our findings in *Science Magazine,* an extremely prestigious journal. Our discovery regarding the effectiveness of artificial reefs in attracting fish led to an ambitious program by the U.S. government in building artificial reefs in the Gulf of Mexico and off the southeastern coast of the United States. The Secretary of the Navy at the time, Paul H. Nitze, awarded us the Meritorious Public Service Citation

HUMAN PERFORMANCE

Human performance included a battery of strength and coordination exercises while diving outside of Sealab II. The engineering tasks assigned to the aquanauts consisted of testing new, thermal wet suits designed for deep and cold submergence, and also several construction and salvage jobs on the ocean floor. One particularly interesting operation was injecting buoyant foam into the hull of a jet airplane that had been placed on the bottom next to the habitat. After several days of foaming and what seemed like an endless stream of liquid plastic, the aircraft lifted off the bottom and floated to the surface. The divers assigned to this job had to be particularly careful not to get tangled in the superstructure during liftoff; any ascent greater than 50 feet off the bottom would have resulted in massive "bends," caused by helium and nitrogen bubbles coming out of solution in the diver's blood. Similarly, any diver who became lost outside the habitat could not have surfaced. All of us were saturated with inert gases.

The advantage of saturation diving, and therefore living on the bottom of the sea in habitats, is that decompression is required only once. Normally, a surface diver working at 205 feet for more than nine minutes would have to spend considerable time decompressing on the way up after each dive. During dives on air or helium-nitrogen-oxygen mixtures, the inert gases are absorbed by the bloodstream in a liquid phase. On

for our research in *Sealab II*. It would greatly help me several years later in landing a job with the Department of Oceanography at the University of Hawai'i.

Sealab II helped open the gates for future exploration of the continental shelves of the world. After 1965, many questions remained unanswered regarding the depth limits of saturation diving, the effects of extended duration, and the psychological effects of living in confined quarters with other divers. Nevertheless, *Sealab I* and *Sealab II,* and the French experiments in undersea living in *Conshelf I, II,* and *III,* all helped to pioneer more advanced undersea technology. They also helped to further tap the enormous wealth of continental shelf resources. Today, divers regularly monitor and operate oil and natural gas wellheads up to 1,500 feet deep in a saturated mode, diving from habitats temporarily moored on the sea bottom. Some predictions about living in underwater cities have not panned out, mainly for economic reasons; the technology, however, has been developed. The future utilization of these tools probably will depend on economic considerations and new research objectives.

We may never travel the depths of the sea in the spirit of Captain Nemo in the *Nautilus,* but it is possible that living under the sea will someday be commonplace. Public undersea observatories already exist in Japan and the Red Sea. Permanent undersea research habitats have also been built in several places around the world, and more are planned. Undersea hotels may become future travel destinations. One such hotel, the Aquarius, is already in the planning stages in Hawai'i. Its centerpiece will be an undersea restaurant. Next time you're in Honolulu, you should come on down and meet the fish.

ascent, these gases must come out of solution and escape slowly through the lungs. If the ascent is too rapid, bubbles form in the bloodstream and divers suffer what is known as decompression sickness, the bends. Dives conducted from Sealab II *to the surrounding bottom normally lasted about one hour. For a dive to 205 feet, for one hour, a diver would have to decompress about 2.5 hours at depths of 30, 20, and 10 feet before surfacing. Diving from a habitat submerged at the depth of repetitive dives avoids decompression until the end of the period of submergence.*

After divers are saturated at a given depth, they can remain there indefinitely without incurring greater decompression debt. One of the major questions that the Sealab II *experiment was designed to answer was whether lengthy saturation produced any physiological problems on the human body. From this standpoint we were indeed guinea pigs.*

Mail from the Aquanauts
SeaLab II
La Jolla, California

Hello up there,

Temperature here is 51°F. Visibility 8 feet. Swell — flat. But plenty da kine fish that is. All is well so far, we will be under for 15 days, this is day 2, still getting oriented to the Helium atmosphere, squeaky voices and headaches. I am studying fish behavior, densities, recruitment, predation, Sea-lab as a fish attractant, effects of lights on same, plankton distribution and behavior and taking multi pictures. We have very little time to sleep so I'll sign off here.
Just to say hello from Under the Sea!

Your Brudda
Ricko

A letter to my sister, Robin

Art by Jo Lathwood

Ron Church photo

8 SURFING OCEANOGRAPHY AND FORECASTING

One after another they come
A mile long with smoking crests
And white battalions
An infinite army of the sea.

Jack London
A ROYAL SPORT: SURFING IN WAIKIKI

My first experience with a wave was almost my last experience in life. My sister Robin had pulled me from the backwash of an overhead (for me) wave in Santa Monica when I was two years old. I have vague memories of being afraid, but probably not so much from the experience as from my mother reminding me later that my sister had saved my life (and, after all, I should be nice to her). Ever since that first experience in the ocean, waves have never ceased to fascinate me.

Waves have stirred the imagination of mankind for millennia. And though their origins are remote, in the vast, open ocean, oceanographers have learned much about their dynamics. In this chapter, the more technical aspects of surfing oceanography are examined—how waves are formed, how big they get, how fast they travel, why they break, and how they are measured. Surf forecasting in particular has become an advanced science. Armed with satellites, ship and stationary buoy reports, and computers, the National Weather Service can predict wave size to the foot and arrival time to the hour.

Wave Characteristics

Surfing waves are generated by wind. The first waves generated by the wind on a flat water surface are called "capillary waves." These are tiny ripples, less than an inch long. If the wind continues to blow, capillary waves grow, transforming the ocean surface into a choppy condition known as "sea." The size that individual waves reach depends on wind speed, wind duration, and the distance over water that the wind blows (fetch). Waves increase in size as a result of the frictional force of wind on individual waves and the pressure difference that the wind sets up between crests and troughs. After seas leave the storm area of their origin, their crests and troughs become smoother and rounder. At that point the waves are called "swell."

All waves are characterized by height, wavelength, period, and speed. The *height* of a wave is the vertical distance between the crest (top) and trough (bottom) of a wave passing a fixed point. The *wavelength* is the horizontal distance between two successive waves. The wave *period* is the time it takes for two successive crests (or troughs) to pass a fixed point, such as a pier. The *speed* of the wave is the speed of energy passing through the water.

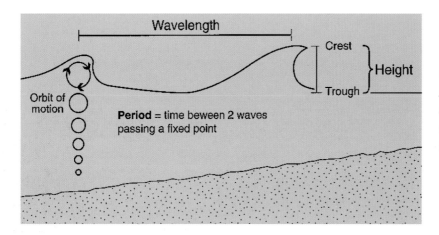

Wavelength, period, and shoaling characteristics of a shallow-water wave; ratio of height to depth is about 1:1

When a wave passes a fixed point, the water lifts up, rotates forward, and then falls back as the wave passes. The water particles inscribe an almost circular orbit while the wave energy continues forward, passing through the medium. The circumference and diameter of the wave orbits are greatest at the surface and progressively diminish with depth. Below a depth equal to one-half the wavelength, the orbits become infinitesimally small.

The height of a wave varies according to how steep it is. Its maximum height occurs at the moment a wave breaks. This is true in either deep or shallow water, although the cause of breaking is not the same. In deep water, waves break because they become unstable. When their height exceeds their wavelength by more than 1:7, deepwater waves become unstable and they topple over. Waves break in shallow water because the speed of the wave (or, in scientific terms, the orbital velocity of the water particles) at the crest exceeds the wave speed at the trough.

Defining wave height may be simple (the vertical distance between the crest and the trough), but it is difficult to measure because the trough, or low point of the wave, is way out in front (or in back) of the crest. The crest and true trough may be separated by several hundred feet. This is one reason that surfers and scientists don't often come up with the same estimate for how big waves are. But before we examine this controversial subject more closely, let's look at some other characteristics of waves.

A wave is considered a deepwater wave if it is traveling in a depth greater than one-half the deepwater wavelength. Shallow-water waves are defined as waves traveling in water shallower than one-twentieth their deepwater wavelength. Waves in between the deep- and shallow-water definition are called "transitional waves." Deepwater waves travel at a velocity equal to their wavelengths divided by their periods (speed = L/T). The greater the ratio of wavelength to period, the greater the speed. For example, waves with wavelengths of 600 feet and 20-second periods travel at 30 feet per second (about 20 mph) at sea.

A storm at sea generates waves with many different wavelengths. Because the velocity of the waves as they move out of the storm depends on their wavelengths, the longer waves travel faster and move ahead of the shorter waves, a process called "dispersion." It results in waves of almost equal wavelength being assembled into groups. When the wave groups reach the shoreline, they are known as "sets." The time in between the arrival of set waves is known as a "lull."

A supertanker leaving San Francisco plows through the crest of a giant comber breaking over the stretch of water called the "Potato Patch." The trough appears to be near the stern of the ship.

Up to this point, we have considered the behavior only of individual waves. In deep water, the life of an individual wave is brief. As it moves ahead in any given group of waves, it gradually disappears and is replaced by a wave from the back of the group. Hence, the speed of the wave group is much less than the speed of the individual waves. Group velocity, in fact, is exactly half the speed of the individual (or phase) velocity. The reason for this is very complex. At the front of a group of waves traveling forward, the ocean surface is relatively undisturbed. The leading wave must disturb the surface ahead to create orbital movement. This requires energy and causes the leading wave to gradually diminish and finally disappear. At the back of the wave group, some energy remains behind the orbits. This excess energy serves to form new waves at the rear of the group. In shallow water, the speed of individual waves (phase speed) slows down as the bottom gets shallower until it is equal to the group velocity. At that point, individual and group velocity is the same. Group velocity in deep water is important in wave forecasting because it is the speed which must be calculated to determine the arrival time of a given swell at a particular shoreline.

Relation of wave height (H), depth of water (d), and wave speed (mph) in shallow water (at a point where the wave breaks, assuming a ratio of H/d of 1.0)

Wave Height (ft)	Depth (ft)	Speed (mph)
5	5	8.6
10	10	12.2
15	15	14.9
20	20	17.2
25	25	19.3
30	30	21.1
35	35	22.8
40	40	24.4
50	50	27.2

In shallow water, the speed of the waves depends on the depth of water and gravity. The formula for their velocity is the square root of gravity times depth: V = the square root of $g \times d$ where $g = 32$ ft/sec^2 and d = water depth in feet. For example, a wave traveling in 10 feet of water will travel the square root of 32 ft/sec$^2 \times 10$ ft = the square root of 320 ft^2/sec^2 = 17.8 ft/sec, or about 12 mph. The accompanying table demonstrates that very large waves, higher than 25 feet, are moving too fast to catch simply by paddling.

Another important characteristic of waves is the water depth where they break. This depends primarily on the slope of the bottom. On gently sloping bottoms that shallow (shoal) slowly, such as Waikīkī Beach, the ratio of wave height to water depth is about 0.7. As the bottom steepness increases, so does the ratio. Where the bottom shoals abruptly, such as Waimea Bay or Jaws, the depth changes from about 80 feet to 30 feet in about 150 feet, which is equivalent to a 20-degree slope. In areas like these, the ratio of wave height to water depth of breaking waves is about 1.2. In such places, a 25-foot wave would break in a water depth of about 21 feet; a 30-foot wave would break in 25 feet of water, and so on. The steeper the bottom, the shallower the break and the more dangerous it gets. Areas with bottom slopes greater than about 30 degrees are unsurfable, because the height-to-depth ratio of breaking waves is too high, with too great a chance of a surfer hitting bottom. The height-to-depth ratio also determines the shape of a breaking wave. Low ratios produce spilling or feathering waves, high ratios produce plunging or tubular waves.

THE GRAVITY OF SURFING

Basically, waves can be surfed because of gravity. Whether using a body, board, canoe, kayak, or boat, the principle remains the same: The surfer slides down the wave face under the force of gravity. Surfing speed is determined by the speed of the wave, the angle of the surfer in the wave, the attack pressure, and surface area drag. Attack pressure is the force rendered to the bottom and edge of the surfing device (board, etc.). For a board surfer, the maximum attack pressure comes during turns, which produce an acceleration force. Thruster three-fin surfboards are faster than single-fin boards because the attack pressure is greater and it is constantly changing.

Gravity is the main reason a surfer can slide down the face of a wave on a surfboard. Ron Church photo.

Surf Forecasting

Surf forecasting is a combination of art and science. Science supplies the factual information, and the art is a measure of a person's ability to interpret the information. Wave height in a storm is determined by wind speed, wind duration, and fetch. The wind speed must be faster than the wave crests for the transfer of energy to the sea to continue; at some point, however, the sea becomes fully developed and will not increase further. In part this is because the wind is blowing the tops off the waves, but more important, it is also caused by waves breaking within the storm as the seas reach the height/wavelength (H/L) ratio of 1:7, where they become unstable and break. Similarly, a sea may become fully developed from duration and fetch. Under these conditions, longer or greater exposure will not increase the size of the waves.

The relation between wind speed, wind duration, and fetch is illustrated in the accompanying graph, called a "nomogram." To calculate the size of waves produced, you must know the wind speed, wind duration, and fetch, as illustrated in the nomogram. For example, a wind of 30 mph blowing for 24 hours over 250 miles of water will produce 12-foot waves. However, if the fetch is only 100 miles, the waves produced will be only 9 feet, a condition called "fetch limited." If the fetch is unlimited and the wind speed is constant, then the duration will determine the ultimate size of the waves. Again, using the example of a 30-mph wind, if its duration were 60 hours and the fetch were unlimited, the waves produced would be 15 feet. If the duration for this example were increased to 80 hours, the maximum waves would be only 16 feet. This example is fast approaching a fully developed sea. The nomogram can be used to determine wave height for any combination of wind speed between 10 and 110 mph, fetch between 1 and 1,000 miles, and duration between 1 and 100 hours. The wave height obtained using this procedure is an average of the largest third ($H_{1/3}$) of the waves produced. This height ($H_{1/3}$) corresponds roughly to the average height of the set waves and is a standard measure used by oceanographers and meteorologists.

After wave height ($H_{1/3}$) has been determined, it is then necessary to calculate the decay that takes place between the storm that produced the waves and their arrival at some distant shoreline. This is difficult, because decay depends on the original fetch and the height of the waves in the storm. A good rule of thumb for decay is about 20 to 25 percent per day. Therefore, 20-foot waves after one day's decay would be about 15 to 16 feet; after two days, about 11 to 13 feet; after three days, about 8 to 10 feet; and so on. The rate of decay could be slightly greater for larger waves. Intervening winds could also make a difference either positively or negatively depending on their direction and strength.

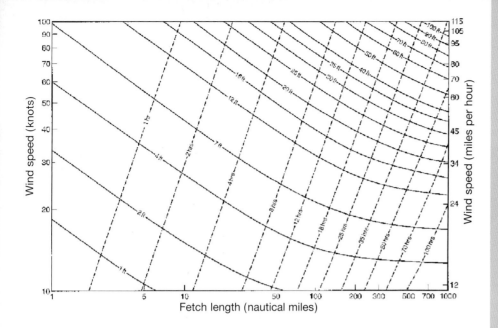

Deepwater forecasting curves for wave height as a function of wind speed, fetch length (distance wind blows over the water), and wind duration (time wind blows). Adapted from Shore Protection Manual, 1973, U.S.A.C.E.

When the waves finally reach their destination, at least two more factors need to be considered: refraction and shoaling. *Refraction* is bending of the wave crests due to the shape and depth of the bottom as the waves advance shoreward. If bending concentrates the wave energy, the waves converge and increase in height. Conversely, if bending spreads out (diverges) the wave energy, wave height decreases. Most big-surf spots are located where convergence is relatively great.

Shoaling transformations take place as waves travel from deep to shallow water before they break. Waves undergo this transformation in depths shallower than one-half their wavelength. At this depth, they are said to begin to "feel" bottom. During the shoaling process, as waves enter progressively shallower water, their energy is concentrated into a smaller and smaller volume of water. This causes an upward movement in the wave energy, and the shape of the wave increases in height and steepness. As a result of shoaling, deepwater wave height may increase by as much as two times. The size of the final breaking wave therefore will depend on the original size of waves produced within the storm ($H_{1/3}$), as well as decay, refraction, and shoaling. A considerable amount of art or local knowledge about individual surf spots is needed to make accurate wave forecasts. For example, on the North Shore of O'ahu, the shoaling factors (which include refraction and shoaling) for Pipeline, Sunset Beach, and Waimea Bay are about 1:6, 1:8, and 2:0, respectively. This means that deepwater waves increase at these locations by 60 percent, 80 percent, and 100 percent, respectively, as they approach the shoreline and break. The direction of the swell is also a factor—it may

THE SWELL OF THE CENTURY

How often do the really big North Pacific swells roll in, and which was the granddaddy of all? It seems to me that about once a decade or so, a truly giant swell reaches Hawai'i. December 22, 1943, when Woody Brown and Dickie Cross got caught outside Sunset Beach, was one of them. Other exceptional days I recall were one in January 1953 (30 feet); March 23, 1974 (40 feet); Super Bowl Sunday, 1988 (35 feet); and Big Wednesday, January 28, 1998 (35 feet). The heights are top to bottom measurements, which means faces up to 60 feet!

Bigger than any of these was the swell that hit Hawai'i on December 2 and 4, 1969. The storm that led up to these waves is pictured on the accompanying weather map. The storm center had a low pressure of 960 millebars. The winds in the 1,200-mile fetch (the boxed area on the map) pointing at Hawai'i were 50 to 60 knots, and they blew for several days. The map represents the time about 60 hours before the peak waves began battering Hawaiian coasts. The largest waves were estimated at 50 feet high, and caused one drowning and $1.5 million in damage in the Hawaiian Islands. Greg Noll caught his famous 35-foot wave at Mākaha during this swell. The same waves when they hit La Jolla, California, three days later, were about 20 feet. I caught a couple of them at La Jolla Cove. It was the biggest day on the coast that anyone could remember.

increase or decrease the shoaling factor on any given day, adding to the complexity of the calculation.

The quality of information initially received can be important in wave forecasting. Sometimes wind speeds reported by mariners at sea will be rough estimates, particularly in a large storm or at night. After a long night on the bridge, a person's estimates of wave height may not be altogether reliable. It therefore requires a little art to interpret incoming data. The consistency of information (swell data) received from ships in a given storm and their agreement with calculations based on wind speed, duration, and fetch may serve as one means of verification.

Measuring Waves

Having discussed the definitions and details of surf forecasting, I would like to turn to the question of exactly how big waves get and how they are measured. The largest wave ever recorded at sea was 112 feet, reported by the USS *Ramapo* in the North Pacific in 1933. This calculation was made by an observer on the bridge who used the angle of the ship and its length to calculate the vertical displacement between the trough and the crest. Winds in the storm that produced this wave were 67 mph, with gusts to 78 mph. If we look at the graph in the text to determine what data would be necessary to produce such a wave, we can see one combination of fetch, wind speed, and duration would be 1,000 miles, 110 mph, and 35 hours, respectively. On the nomogram, larger fetches and greater wind speeds go off-scale. In the real world, however, maximum wind speeds in the largest storms that produce the biggest waves are usually in the

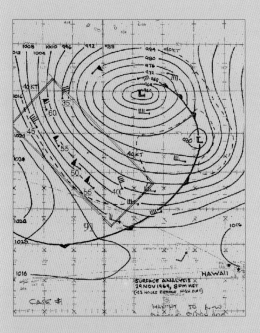

Weather map of the storm on November 29, 1969, at 8:00 P.M. HST, that produced exceptional surf in Hawai‘i on December 2 and 4, 1969

I caught one of the huge waves at La Jolla Cove, California, on December 7, 1969. This surf was produced by the same storm that had raised mammoth surf in Hawai‘i three days earlier. Photographer unknown.

85

60 to 80 mph range, somewhat less than the 110 mph in the chart. Given real-world limits, the 112-foot wave measured by the *Ramapo* is probably a fairly good estimate of the largest wave that can be produced in any ocean.

What about the largest wave ever surfed? First, exact height is difficult to pin down; it may be safer to express the number as a range. For waves caught paddling, 30 to 35 feet would seem a fair estimate. A famous wave caught by Greg Noll on December 4, 1969, at Mākaha was estimated at 35 feet by those who saw it. In the pioneering years of surfing, in the 1950s and '60s, Buzzy Trent and Peter Cole were also credited with catching a 30-foot-plus wave. Since then Ken Bradshaw, Brock Little, Darrick Doerner, and Mark Foo have joined the 30-foot-plus club, unless you begin to talk about tow-in surfing.

Tow-in surfing consists of a boat or jet ski pulling a surfer into a wave with a towline (see chapter 17 for a detailed description of the equipment and technique of tow-in surfing). The main point to consider here is that riders are pulled into massive swells at speeds much greater than

A huge "First Break" summer swell at Waikīkī Beach in 1949. Joe Quigg photo.

WHY THE BIGGEST SURF IN HAWAI'I OCCURS IN WINTER

Stories of monster summer surf off Waikīkī on the south shore of O'ahu are legendary in the history of Hawai'i surfing. Stories about Waikīkī's famous surf have circulated for years, but most of these tales originated long before anyone attempted to surf the mammoth waves on the northern shores of the Islands. One famous story of summer surf recounts Duke Kahanamoku riding a 20-foot wave one and one-eighth miles from Castle's Break off Diamond Head all

a person ever could paddle. Waves are caught early, at 25 to 30 mph, allowing time for the tow-in surfer to drop the towline and penetrate well down the face before the wave becomes vertical. Previously, this was the limiting factor in riding big waves higher than 30 feet—paddling fast enough to catch the wave and getting far enough down the face before it became vertical. Overcoming this hurdle has opened the gates of big-wave surfing to waves virtually as big as they get. Already, Laird Hamilton has successfully ridden 35-footers if not bigger. The October 1996 issue of *Surfer* magazine—"The Future is Now" issue—pictures Laird on a 50-footer at a mythical place called Foo's in the year 2012. My guess is that he will catch one this big in the next couple of years—unless he dies trying.

Almost no surfer measures waves the simple way—the way oceanographers do—from the crest to the trough. Many reasons account for this. As described above, the crest and trough are difficult to see at the same time, because the trough is way out ahead of the crest. Surfers find it much easier to estimate the face of a wave. But the face is constantly changing, depending on wave steepness. This forces some surfers to measure waves from the back. From shore, though, you cannot see the back! And don't discount the social pressures and peer-group acceptance problems. Macho types estimate big waves on the small size, and wimps copy them. People in different localities—Californians, Hawaiians, East Coasters, Aussies—make estimates using different guidelines. Almost no one agrees with anyone else. Jonathan Hoag, a meteorologist and wave forecaster at the Honolulu Office of the National Weather Service, was so amused by all the confusion that he posted the question "How do you measure a wave?" on the Internet. The following are some of the answers he received:

> "Top two-thirds as seen from the beach."
> "Estimate crest to trough in feet and divide by two."
> "Knee high, waist high, head high, double overhead, and so on."
> "Who really gives a damn?"
> "Cut the face in half and subtract a foot. This really irks people who have an attachment to reality."
> "Just make up a good lie like everybody else."
> "We measure from the back. I know it's stupid but everybody does it."
> "Three feet is head high, six is double overhead."
> "Riding Waimea is like dropping down a 50- to 75-foot face."

Maybe it is easier simply to measure from crest to trough. If this doesn't appeal to you, do it your own way. Hanalei, a famous beachboy in Waikīkī, has figured it out: "When it come to judging waves, 'Everybody is right.'"

the way to Baby Queen's, close to the old Moana Hotel. Accounts of even bigger summer surf, up to 25 feet, are also told about a break farther out beyond Castle's. Its name is Papanui, or Steamer's Lane. It lies in blue water out where ships round the point at Diamond Head on the way into Honolulu Harbor. I've been surfing for about forty years in Hawai'i, and I've never seen it break. Old-timers like Woody Brown and John Kelly, though, and some of the early Waikīkī beachboys, swear that 25-foot waves have been ridden there, back in the 1940s or even earlier. Kelly claims that summer surf back then was even bigger than the North Shore waves.

I don't like to refute these nostalgic accounts of heroics from years gone by, but I do think it is interesting to look at the oceanographic likelihood of rideable waves this big hitting the south shore. Applying what is known of ocean storms in the Pacific and how waves decay as they move across open ocean, rideable summer waves at Waikīkī bigger than about 15 feet or at most 18 feet are highly unlikely. Let's look at the details.

The north and northwest shores of the Hawaiian Islands receive the largest rideable surf in the world for three reasons. First, the Pacific Ocean not only is the largest ocean in the world but it also contains the longest fetch (distance over water that winds blow) areas in the world. Fetch areas up to 1,500 miles are not uncommon. The second reason has to do with the difference between water and air temperature at the ocean surface in the

Rogue Waves and Tsunamis

A rogue wave to a layman may simply mean an out-of-the-ordinary big one, but to an oceanographer, rogue waves are defined as "extreme storm waves" and are known to reach heights 2.5 times greater than the highest one-third of the waves in a given storm. Exactly how big this might be has not been documented other than by the ships they have sunk. Examples include the 117-foot *Marques*, which went down in the Atlantic in the 1960s, drowning eighteen of twenty-seven crew members. Another is the *Holoholo*, which sank with ten oceanographers on board during a fierce Hawaiian storm in 1978.

Several mechanisms may produce rogue waves. One may be conditions where extremes in wave size and current run in opposite directions, producing extremely steep waves with deep troughs. This occurs off the southeast coast of Africa, where the southerly flowing Algulhas Current meets the famous "Cape rollers" heading north. The result is chaos.

Another cause of extreme storm waves is the intersection of two or more waves when they merge in a confused sea. These waves are usually short-lived; in fact, they often may cancel one another. High seas formed in this way are usually confined to areas near or within storms. Intense typhoons or hurricanes of small diameter will often generate waves in all directions, some of which inevitably collide. While such waves may last only a minute or so, they are capable of reaching heights near 100 feet and overturning large ships.

Another phenomenon that may produce superwaves is atmospheric downbursts. A downburst is an intense gust of cold, dense air plummeting downward along a squall front and striking the surface of the sea. Such downbursts may come in rapid succession. When they occur over land, they can produce a swath of destruction 100 miles wide or more. Much less is known about the waves they may produce at sea.

Perhaps the only good news about rogue waves is that they are usually confined to storm areas at sea, and they are rare phenomena. They are not likely to strike a shoreline and are even less likely to be ridden by surfers, rogue or otherwise. We should probably classify them as unrideable, at least until some crazy surfer catches one.

Speaking of crazy surfers, I should say a word or two about tsunamis. Tsunamis, or so-called tidal waves, are produced by earthquakes. They travel at great speeds (500 mph) across the ocean, have large wavelengths (about 100 miles long), and periods upward to fifteen minutes. Large tsunamis can be enormously destructive and dangerous. On May 22, 1960, a huge tsunami slammed into Hilo, Hawai'i, causing sixty-one deaths and $15 million damage. In the city of Hilo the wave reached 37 feet above sea level. The cause of the tsunami was a massive earthquake along the Peru-

region of storm formation in the far northwestern sector off Japan. In that area, a unique confluence of warm water and cold wind exists at mid-latitudes, caused by the meeting of the northward-flowing warm Kuroshio Current and winds blowing off northern Asia. The Kuroshio is a swift, narrow current beginning approximately at the latitude of the northern Philippine Islands and heading north all the way to Japan before turning eastward across the Pacific, where it is known as the North Pacific Drift. It transports huge amounts of heat into the northern Pacific. Cold winds blowing off the Asian continent collide with the warm waters of the Kuroshio and North Pacific Drift and together form the ingredients for a cauldron that spawns storms larger than anywhere else on the planet. The warm water is the heat engine of the storms. Heat supplies the energy for evaporation and the transfer of latent heat to the atmosphere. The air rapidly rises, creating low pressure and strong surface winds. The size of the low-pressure systems and the strength of their winds depend on the magnitude of the forces that produce them. In the Atlantic, the Gulf Stream meeting cold winds blowing southeast from Canada produces a similar set of conditions, but affects smaller areas than in the Pacific. In the Indian Ocean and the southern Pacific Ocean, no such comparable area exists where cold wind and warm water come into such close contact.

Oceanography therefore "predicts" that the source of the biggest surf in

Felipe Pomar, ready to catch any giant wave except another tsunami. Photo courtesy of Felipe Pomar.

Chile trench. Hawai'i is hit by a significant tsunami about once every ten or twenty years. At this writing (1998), we are long overdue for a big one.

Tsunamis are definitely not recommended for surfing, though it is not impossible to do so. Felipe Pomar, the 1968 world champion surfer from Peru, once rode a small one in his home country by accident while trying to reach shore. I asked Felipe what it was like to have ridden a tsunami, and he described it as a total nightmare of churning water. He just hung on to his board for dear life and somehow washed up onshore. It was his last tsunami.

Epilogue

Joseph Conrad wrote, "The sea never changes, and its works for all the talk of men, are wrapped in mystery." My discussion of surfing oceanography may have dispelled some, but not all, of the mystery. Part of what we feel about the ocean is unknowable. It lies in the realm of our emotions, perhaps as a place from which we evolved. Our blood still carries a vestige of the ocean's salinity. The sea is also a place for great emotional encounters. And for some people, it is a proving ground for riding yet a bigger wave or maybe even conquering a rogue wave. Perhaps how we measure such waves is a subconscious measure of ourselves; it is a test of mankind against nature, and at the same time it reflects the harmony between us.

the world will be the North Pacific. The third reason why summer surf in Hawai'i is smaller than winter surf has to do with the decay distance from storms in the Southern Hemisphere, where the waves are produced. This is on the order of 4,000 miles. In the North Pacific, the decay distance usually is only 1,000 to 2,000 miles. Waves typically travel about 600 miles a day and lose about 20 percent of their energy. Hence, the travel time and energy loss for waves coming from the Southern Hemisphere to Hawai'i is about six to seven days and 80 percent, respectively. Similar figures for waves generated by North Pacific storms are one to three days, with only 20 to 50 percent loss.

Occasionally, hurricanes pass extremely close to the Islands, sometimes even registering a direct hit. The waves they produce may be huge and highly destructive, but they are almost always unrideable. It is therefore unlikely (though not impossible) that the great waves of Papanui are from this source. A better explanation might be that their size in the old days was greatly exaggerated, and with the passing of time, they've become even bigger.

9 WINNING THE DUKE

Heroing is one of the shortest-lived professions there is.

Will Rogers

Winning the Duke Kahanamoku Invitational surfing contest in 1967 was the biggest sports thrill of my life. It was no ordinary surfing contest. Named after its founder, in the early years The Duke was the ultimate world surfing contest, though this was to change rapidly. Why The Duke contest was so important to surfing can be linked both to the history and the future of the sport at that time. Duke Kahanamoku was still alive. He had been Hawai'i's most famous athlete and waterman for more than fifty years. He had won gold or silver medals in swimming in three Olympic Games: 1912 in Stockholm; 1920 in Antwerp; and 1924 in Paris. In the 1912 Games, Duke shaved a full 3 seconds off the world record and won the gold in the 100-meter freestyle. During those early years of the twentieth century, Duke introduced surfing to many places around the world, notably in Freshwater, Sydney, Australia, in 1915 and in Ocean City, New Jersey, in 1918. Duke's legendary exploits included using his surfboard to save eight people from drowning in rough seas off Newport Beach, California, in 1925. His legendary mile-long rides on his 114-pound surfboard from outside Castle's to the Moana Hotel in Waikīkī are feats that rarely have been duplicated, even to this day. Duke Kahanamoku was the father of modern-day surfing the world over. The contest named for him symbolized the early history of the sport.

In 1967, surfing was undergoing a radical transition, from being a way of life to becoming serious competition accompanied by serious commercialism. In the late 1950s and early '60s, surf films caught on in Hawai'i and California. The film media was joined by other forms of commercialism, such as surf magazines and surf music. Surfers were beginning to receive endorsements from all kinds of surf-related companies. Most of the media hype focused on hotdogging and small surf in California. Riding the big surf in Hawai'i attracted less attention. Some-

Duke Kahanamoku greeting me at the Honolulu airport in 1967. Photo courtesy of the Honolulu Advertiser.

Greg Noll, Felipe Pomar, Fred Hemmings, and I (right to left) assess the surf minutes before paddling out for the final heat of the second annual Duke Kahanamoku contest in early 1967. Leroy Grannis photo.

Competitive surfing in Hawai'i predates the arrival of Captain Cook. Competition and wagering among the Hawaiian royalty over their surfing skills is a documented fact. The most prolific surfer reaped rewards and honors.

Modern-day surfing competitions began in 1954 with the Mākaha International, which grew throughout the 1950s as such champions as George Downing, Rabbit Kekai, and Peter Cole made their mark in the world of competitive surfing. The event continued to grow in stature and size into the early 1960s, with the likes of Paul Strauch, Joey Cabell, and Fred Hemmings emerging as champions. With the surfing boom of the early 1960s, contests flourished and became known as a means to recognize the best surfers. In 1964 the first amateur World Championships were held in Sydney, Australia, with Bernard "Midget" Farrelly taking the inaugural title. It was followed the next year in Lima, Peru, where Felipe Pomar was crowned the winner.

Hawai'i, with its huge, demanding surf, was still regarded as the preeminent surfing spot. In the winter of 1965, entrepreneur Kimo McVay introduced the first major event on the North Shore of O'ahu—the Duke Kahanamoku Hawaiian Surfing Invitational, named for the patriarch of Hawaiian surfing. With fanfare, flourish, and a field of twenty-four elite riders, along with a venue of

how it held on to its roots, its image as an alternative lifestyle. In 1967, The Duke was a nonprofessional event—no prize money was offered. It was held in the biggest rideable surf possible. Also, being an invitational, only twenty-four of the world's best surfers were invited to compete. It attracted a little media coverage, but the contest had a nostalgic flavor of days gone by, of a time represented by the Duke himself.

An invitation to The Duke meant a round-trip ticket to Hawai'i and one week at the Royal Hawaiian Hotel, all expenses paid. Surfers were flown in from around the world and were picked up at the airport in a white Rolls Royce. Dinners before and after the contest were at the famous Duke's Restaurant in Honolulu. All competitors received a "passport" to the Hawaiian Islands issued by Duke Paoa Kahanamoku for all privileges described in it, which included dinner with the Duke and an evening at the Don Ho show in Waikīkī. The entire event was a class act, from start to finish. For years Fred Van Dyke, the meet director, had dreamed of holding an Olympic Games–caliber event in big surf at Sunset Beach, Hawai'i. The Duke competition made Fred's dream come true.

When I received my invitation to surf in The Duke, it was the winter of 1966–1967, my third year in graduate school at Scripps. I had been warned about competing other than in my studies at Scripps, but this was simply too good to pass up. By then, I had eight winters' experience (off and on) in big surf on the North Shore of Oʻahu. Furthermore, the site chosen for the contest, Sunset Beach, was my favorite spot. The February 1967 meet was the second annual Duke Invitational. I had been invited in 1965, but the date fell in the middle of my final exams at Scripps. This time I was not going to miss out.

The morning of the contest, February 1, all the competitors received an early wake-up call at the Royal. After hot coffee and some pastries, all twenty-four surfers were herded into a chartered bus with Sunset Beach as the destination. When we crested the hill in the sugarcane fields above Haleʻiwa and caught our first glimpse of the surf, everyone yelled. We could see it was up, really up. Avalanche, the break outside Haleʻiwa, was going off at 18 feet plus. Sunset would be all-time.

Sunset Beach is the most difficult big-wave surf spot in Hawaiʻi to line up. Waimea Bay is bigger and Banzai Pipeline is hollower, but Sunset has a reputation for being the toughest wave to catch—the peak is constantly shifting, sometimes north, sometimes west, ranging over about 250 yards of reef. It takes years of experience before a surfer gets it "wired."

the challenging surf at Sunset Beach, "The Duke" in its inaugural year replaced the Mākaha International as the premier surfing event in the world.

During the same time a short-board revolution had begun, with Nat Young winning the Amateur World Championships in San Diego in 1966. The winter of 1966–1967 was the last year of the long board. It marked the end of the era for dominance by the first North Shore surfers and signaled the beginning of the short-board influence, a surfing counterculture, and a fledgling move toward professionalism. The halcyon days of The Duke were 1965 through

Sunset on the day of the '67 Duke was classic—15 plus, clean, hollow, and hairy.

On one wave in the finals, I got tubed three times.

I had figured out a lineup at Sunset Beach that no one else seemed to understand. Three deep reefs lie 400 to 500 yards out beyond the main break. Set waves "indicate" over these reefs in a telltale way, predicting where they will break on the inner reefs. The trick is in reading the signs. My secret was this area, called the West Peak.

As a full-time student in California, I had only limited training for The Duke that year. At Scripps, I surfed almost every day at lunchtime. On days when it was flat, I went diving under the pier for halibut (breath-holding while skin diving was another important way to train for big-wave wipeouts). More important, I also had those eight winters at Sunset Beach and the accumulated wave knowledge that went with them. A lot of that knowledge came from chasing waves on the West Peak.

As the bus rolled into the parking lot at Sunset Beach, everyone was buzzing with excitement. The surf was 12 to 18 feet, with a 20-knot offshore wind. It was huge and gnarly, but clean. Out of the corner of my eye, I saw the West Peak going off; my strategy was set.

Fred Van Dyke had explained the rules of the contest to us on the bus. We would be judged on our best five waves, 20 points maximum

1969, *though the event continued into the early 1980s.*

In 1968 the amateur World Championships were run in Puerto Rico, with Fred Hemmings emerging victorious. The 1970 event was held in Victoria, Australia, with newcomer Rolf Aurness taking the title. While some minor prize money had been put up as early as 1968 and 1969, the winter of 1970–1971 saw the introduction of serious prize money with the Smirnoff Pro-Am, held at various locales, followed by the Pipeline Masters in 1971 (which up until then had been regarded as too dangerous for competition). These new pro events, combined with a new breed of performers, such as Jeff Hakman, Barry Kanaiaupuni, and Gerry Lopez, as well as advances in equipment, set the stage for a new mentality in the surfing world. With it, the amateur world titles were left behind in the wake of prize money, and professional surfing became established as the new order. Hawai'i remained the centerpiece, but surfing events sprang up around the world, from Africa to Asia, requiring the formation of a world sanctioning and rating body. In 1975 the International Professional Surfing (IPS) world pro circuit tour was formed by former world champion, turned promoter, Fred Hemmings.

The money has increased, the venues have changed, the stars have come and gone, but international contests have remained more or less the same. A single contest no longer distinguishes the best in the world. A world pro tour singles out the

per wave, 100 points total. Scores in the preliminary heats would be added to points earned in the semifinals and finals for those advancing surfers. Points would be awarded for length of ride, time in the tunnel, and overall control and performance. We would be given forty-five minutes in the heats and one hour in the final. At nine o'clock we hit the water.

My early heats were good but not outstanding. I was out of practice for big Sunset. Luckily, I squeaked into the semifinals, and then I began feeling like my old self at Sunset. I began working the West Peak, sitting outside and picking up the biggest waves ahead of everyone else, fading left and then coming around right for some of the longest rides of the day. It was enough to get me into the finals—and then I began to get nervous. I hadn't seriously thought about winning. I was one of the older surfers in the meet, and winning didn't seem probable. My competition for the finals included Mike Doyle, Fred Hemmings, Felipe Pomar, Jock Sutherland, Eddie Aikau, Ben Aipa, Greg Noll, and Mike Hynson—eight of the best surfers in the world. Fred Hemmings and Felipe Pomar had won two early world championships in Puerto Rico and Peru, respectively. Mike Doyle had won more contests overall than any other competitor in The Duke. Jock Sutherland, Eddie Aikau, and Ben Aipa were three of the hottest "up-and-comers" in the sport anywhere in the world. Greg Noll was the heavy of all heavies when it came to big waves. And Mike Hynson was one of the smoothest hotdoggers from California at the time. The idea of me winning was fairly far fetched.

My only hope was the West Peak. When the horn sounded for the finals to begin, I made a beeline straight out and over to the west. Sure enough, the other surfers were clustering around the middle and north peaks. What happened that day is history. Luck was on my side. I caught about ten waves during the final heat. Two were scored perfectly by all three judges. They were 18-footers on the West Peak and lined up perfectly as they moved inside. I got tubed on both, once three times in rapid succession. The other waves also were major set waves coming off the West Peak. It was one of my best days ever at Sunset Beach. By the end of the heat, I knew I had won the contest. Somehow, concentrating on the ocean and not thinking too much about what the other guys were

best of the best, with Hawai'i's Triple Crown of Surfing series hosting the final events of the Association of Surfing Professionals (ASP, successor to the IPS) tour, which showcases Hawai'i's winter surf. The tour, as it moves into the twenty-first century— with more than $350,000 in prize money in Hawai'i alone and nearly $4 million on the world tour—has turned surfing into big business.

Today, surfing has pro events, long-board events, body-board events, amateur events, windsurfing events, and even tow-in events. People compete at all age levels. The women's circuit is nearly as big as the men's and equally popular. Today, thirty years after it all began, winning in Hawai'i in front of your peers is still the ultimate competitive accomplishment.

doing made it all feel natural. My old pals Mike Doyle and Fred Hemmings came in second and third.

After the '67 Duke, my surfing career gradually wound down. I was invited to enter the next Duke meet, but it didn't seem the same, even though I came in second behind Mike Doyle. Duke Kahanamoku was by then gravely ill and could not join us at the contest. And the competition itself had changed. The third Duke was the first year prize money was awarded; it had become a professional contest. We were no longer put up at the Royal Hawaiian Hotel. No white Rolls Royce. Increased media coverage. NBC's *Wide World of Sports* covered the event, which was later aired to 40–50 million viewers. It seemed that big-wave riding was falling more and more under the influence of the media and losing that original man-against-the-sea feeling.

The Duke contest continued for another dozen years before being

Bruce Brown interviewing the Duke and me at the awards ceremony after the contest, with Mike Doyle and Fred Hemmings looking on

superseded by the Smirnoff Pro-Am and eventually the Triple Crown of Surfing. Big-wave riding is still a sport that appeals to the most rugged of individuals. But surfing overall has become highly professional. The Duke contest captured a bit of the old while ushering in the new. It was a time of transition for the sport of surfing and for my life as well. For me, it was an opportunity to do it one more time, to win one for the Gipper. Today as I watch the Kelly Slaters and the Sunny Garcias I marvel at their athleticism. Their skill level makes me feel like someone from the Dark Ages, but it's thrilling to watch them. An even better feeling settles over me when I think back to that day on February 1, 1967, when Sunset Beach smiled on me. When the Duke handed me the trophy at the ceremony after the contest, he said, "Ricky, you really understand the ocean." At that moment, I felt my strategy of life, of surfing, and oceanography all come together.

Jeff Hakman (winner of the first Duke) and me posing with the Duke and the perpetual trophy

The International Surfing *magazine top surfer poll of* 1968

Conducting a survey of the black coral bed off Maui in Star II

10 DIVE, DIVE, DIVE FOR CORAL TREASURE

The price of wisdom is above rubies. JOB 28:18

From the day when I was eight years old and saw the movie *Drums of Pago Pago* I always wanted to dive for treasure. Probably like striking it rich in Las Vegas, the idea was more fantasy than something I thought I would actually do. Instead, I chose a career in marine science, thinking it might lead to a real job; I could at least study about treasure. And that's exactly what happened.

Studying Coral Becomes My Job

After college at Stanford, and my surfing and Tahiti sabbatical, I spent three years studying black coral at the University of Hawai'i on my way to earning a master's degree. Black coral is a highly prized "gemstone" of the sea, used for making exotic jewelry in many countries around the world. I continued in this vein at Scripps Institution of Oceanography, where I studied deep-sea coral biology for another five years, this time for a Ph.D. It added up to a lot of years studying, but one spin-off to being a student for so long was the unstructured time it gave me to keep surfing. And by studying oceanography, I was assured of always being on a coastline somewhere in the world, where there would be waves. Because I had chosen corals as the subject of my Ph.D. dissertation, these coastlines more than likely would be somewhere in the Tropics.

I was therefore elated when I received a letter in the fall of 1969 offering me a position in the Department of Oceanography at the University of Hawai'i. This was good fortune, but I also recalled two earlier letters rejecting my applications. My admissions into Stanford and Scripps had required second efforts (an associate of arts degree from junior college for Stanford, and a master's degree from the University of Hawai'i for Scripps). Whatever doubts I had about my ability to become an ocean-ographer were compensated by trying just that much harder.

MEDUSA'S GIFT

The story begins with Perseus, the son of Zeus. Perseus' mother, Danae, had been kidnapped by an evil king named Polydectes, who lived on the island of Seriphos in the Aegean Sea. The task of rescuing her had been given to Perseus by the gods on Mount Olympus. When Perseus arrived on Seriphos he discovered King Polydectes was planning to take Danae against her will as his bride. To get rid of Perseus, King Polydectes launched a plot. Before he would allow Perseus to see his mother, Perseus would have to first prove his worthiness: He must slay the Gorgon Medusa. Everyone in the land knew that the Medusa was so hideously ugly that anyone who looked at her was instantly turned to stone. How was Perseus to kill the Gorgon with his eyes closed? Meanwhile, the gods on Mount Olympus had been listening. Wasting no time, they sent the messenger Hermes, armed with wisdom and magic, to counsel Perseus. Hermes bestowed upon Perseus three weapons: winged sandals, a polished shield, and a razor-sharp sword. The sandals would give Perseus flight, the shield would cover his eyes and be a mirror in which he could see the Gorgon, and the sword would be used to sever her head. As luck would have it, when Perseus arrived at the dragon's

The job in Hawai'i sounded like the sequel to *Drums of Pago Pago*. It was to head a research program on the ecology of precious coral. Precious corals consist of a family of deepwater corals, including black and pink coral and the famous "red coral of commerce." The skeletons of these species are very hard (nonporous) and lustrous, and can be polished into beautiful jewelry.

Precious Coral

The luster of precious coral was first discovered by Palaeolithic man. Excavations of archaeological gravesites in central Germany, dated about 25,000 years ago, contain polished beads of red coral. Some of the beads were even perforated. Stone Age man buried his dead with their most treasured possessions. We don't know if the beads were used primarily for trade (money) or decoration, but precious corals evidently have been objects of value to humans since the dawn of civilization.

Red coral lives in the Mediterranean Sea at depths between 30 and 900 feet. Broken pieces of red coral may have been cast up by the sea, wave-worn and shiny, on ancient Aegean beaches. There, the sun's reflection may have struck the eye of a Palaeolithic boy. Or perhaps it was curiosity or even romance in the eye of the first person to see its beauty that led to its use. Whatever that moment, the feeling persisted down through the ages, and precious coral became firmly established as a gemstone in the culture of primitive man. The Greeks eulogized its special value by inventing a myth to give it an extraordinary origin, the myth of Perseus and the Gorgon Medusa.

The job at the University of Hawai'i studying corals in the Pacific led me on a series of great adventures. Having studied the ecology of deep-water corals for my Ph.D. at Scripps, for me it was truly the perfect job, not to mention the location. Becoming an oceanographer in Hawai'i was my high school dream come true. Now all I had to do was to be one.

The next ten years were filled with exploration and discovery. Early on, I teamed up with Maui Divers of Hawai'i, a small company headed by Cliff Slater that would one day be the largest manufacturer of precious coral jewelry in the world. The first few years, our only tools of exploration were dredges and a deep-camera sled that we could lower from the surface ship. A video camera on the sled transmitted a black-and-white image of the bottom up to our ship in real time. We could see the coral beds below us down to 1,000 meters (about 3,000 feet) depth. The dredges consisted of weighted tangle nets. From the University of Hawai'i ship *Teritu*, we photographed and dredged the flanks of every island and volcano in the Hawaiian Archipelago, covering more than 1,400 miles of terrain. In total we discovered ninety-three species of deep coral. Twelve were new to science altogether, and twenty-four were new zoogeographic records for the Hawaiian Islands. Five new beds of precious coral containing commercial quantities of pink, gold, and bamboo corals were discovered at depths near 1,200 feet. These would later be mined with a mini-submarine. In shallower water, we mapped six beds of black coral off the islands of Hawai'i, Maui, Lāna'i, O'ahu, and Kaua'i. North of Kaua'i, cool waters prevail at the depths where black corals live (between 150 and 350 feet), limiting their distribution and abundance.

Black coral had been discovered off Maui in 1958 by Jack Ackerman and Larry Windley. Ackerman and Windley had founded Maui Divers with black-coral jewelry as their main product. I worked for them as a diver in the early 1960s, when all of the beds were in a virgin state. I could

A painting of the Gorgon Medusa photographed by the author in the Uffizzi Gallery in Florence, Italy

lair, Medusa was sleeping. Her snake hair was writhing, but the rest of her enormous body lay flaccid and still. Descending in the air above her, with her neck clearly reflected on his shield, he let fly a mighty blow with his magic sword. The head fell instantly to the floor of the cave; Perseus darted down, grabbed it, and stuffed it into a leather pouch. In seconds, Perseus was high in the sky, flying back to Seriphos and the court of King Polydectes. He arrived just as the wedding was about to begin and demanded that he be allowed to prove the success of his mission. King Polydectes in disbelief was too curious to reject his plea. Perseus burst forward with his proof. Whispering to his mother to cover her eyes, he pulled the Gorgon's head from his leather pouch and held it high for all to see. Instantly, King Polydectes and his entire court of nobles were turned to stone.

As Perseus returned to Mount Olympus, with no further need for Medusa's head, he cast it into the sea. Again its magical powers were manifested, this time turning the soft algae into stone. Blood from the Gorgon head dyed the stony algae red, giving rise to red coral. Minerva, the sister of Perseus, was so pleased with her brother's exploits that she conferred magical properties upon red coral. The ancients thus came to believe that red coral protected them from the Evil Eye, that it guarded them against stings and poisons and gout, that it even gave them immortality. It was Medusa's gift to the ancient world.

Mike Palmgren and Steve Dollar measure the growth of black coral at 180 feet off Lahaina, Maui.

see the beds might not last forever and gradually began studying their ecology. At first, I tagged a few small colonies at a place called Stone Wall, where we frequently dived. From this simple experiment, I later expanded the study into the research for my master's degree at the University of Hawai'i.

Maui Divers gradually increased in size during the early '60s with the addition of Cliff Slater and John Stewart. Their history, however, was not without human tragedy. Larry Windley left the partnership in 1960 after being paralyzed by the bends. Several years later, he sailed out to sea in a 15-foot catamaran, never to be seen again. The partnership split up in 1963 with Cliff Slater and John Stewart moving to Honolulu and Jack Ackerman keeping the retail store in Lahaina. John Stewart sold his share of the business and subsequently shot himself. Jack Ackerman eventually sold his store to his wife, Janie, and, heading for the South Pacific, ended up in the Kingdom of Tonga. By 1970, when I returned to the University of Hawai'i to begin a study of deepwater precious corals, Maui Divers was under the firm control of Cliff Slater. One year later, Slater would help the University of Hawai'i purchase a two-man submarine, the *Star II,* to aid in our research efforts.

Star II *Submersible*

My first dive in *Star II* was with Boh Bartko in the Makapu'u pink coral bed to a depth of 1,200 feet. It was Thursday, September 9, 1971. In Hawai'i, it was the first dive in history to this depth. Boh and I were nervous about the danger of diving into an unknown place and depth, but we were also excited—much more excited—about what we would find. As Boh closed up the hatch, locking us inside the 4-foot-diameter steel hull, we were inescapably committed. He reached forward for the sub-to-ship radio and said, "We're ready to dive, dive, dive."

As we approached the bottom, Boh radioed to the surface, "In sight, in sight—we've got the bottom in sight." My notes in my research log for that day read as follows: "While Boh adjusted our buoyancy in order to make a soft landing on the bottom, I gaped out my side port in wonder. The floodlights lit up the bottom in an otherwise pitch dark ocean. It was covered by corals of all kind and color: gold, pink, red, bamboo, blue, and green. It was a vast treasure trove of precious coral. The depth gauge read 1,150 feet. The temperature outside was a chilly 10 degrees centigrade (50 degrees Fahrenheit). I was glad I had brought along a sweater."

That day we discovered a huge bed of pink coral covering 3 square miles of ocean bottom. It contained about 40,000 to 50,000 kilograms of pink coral valued at $200/kg, or about $10 million. We also discovered gold and bamboo coral, which were less abundant and less valuable than pink coral but new to science. Over the next three years, we would map the bed and measure the growth and turnover rates (mortality and recolonization) of those species of commercial value. We developed a Federal Fishery Management Plan that limited the amount of harvest to 1,000 kg a year, approximately 2 percent of the standing crop of the pink coral. In 1975, Maui Divers leased the *Star II* submarine from the University of Hawai'i and converted it into a commercial operation.

The transfer of the *Star II* to Maui Divers had been part of the original plan. One goal of our federal research grant was to begin a commercial fishery. Handing over the results of tax-supported research to private industry is an inherent objective of all government-funded research. Our job was to create opportunities, not to benefit from them. That returned the tax dollars to the states and to the taxpayers. The economic benefits that accrued to the precious coral industry over the years of our research included a pattern of steady growth from about $2 million in 1970 to tens of millions of dollars in the eighties and nineties. More than one thousand jobs in the state of Hawai'i are connected with the precious coral industry today. It has been a story of success, though not without accident and loss of human life.

Pink, gold, and bamboo coral at 1,300 feet off Makapu'u, O'ahu. David Doubilet photo.

The worst accident occurred on September 6, 1975. Maui Divers had been operating *Star II* in the Makapuʻu coral bed and elsewhere off Hawaiʻi and Maui for about four years without mishap. The system included a mother ship, the submarine, and a launching platform called the LRT, short for "launch, recovery, and transport." It was a barge of sorts, used to tow the submarine behind the mother ship. When a dive site was reached, the LRT served as an underwater launching pad. Equipped with two large pontoons on either side of the barge, it could be submerged by flooding both chambers. A team of three divers then controlled the descent to a depth of about 60 feet, where the submarine would be unhooked and free to lift off and dive. At the completion of a dive, the reverse procedure would recover the submarine underwater. This procedure allowed for launch and recovery operations to proceed even during very rough seas, which typify Hawaiian weather. Maui Divers had conducted hundreds of safe dives until that one fateful day.

The weather on that day was marginal, 25- to 30-knot winds and 12- to 15-foot seas in the channels. The operation had become so routine,

Two Maui Divers operate the LRT while recovering the Star II *after a productive dive to the bottom for pink and gold coral at* 1,250 *feet in the Makapuʻu bed.*

though, that plans to dive were not canceled. The men had dived under these conditions many times before. In fact, the LRT had been planned and built for the very purpose of handling this kind of weather—except for one thing: the change in pressure that takes place with huge overhead seas. That day the launching team took *Star II* to 90 feet before unhooking the sub. Even at that depth the seas overhead were creating a vertical surge of 5 to 10 feet between waves. At the precise moment the sub lifted off, the LRT surged downward. Ricky Inada estimates it dropped about 10 feet. Suddenly, one buoyancy chamber on the left side imploded. The LRT instantly began sinking, very fast. The other two divers sprinted down to repressurize the remaining three buoyancy pontoons. As they worked feverishly, Ricky saw them slowly disappearing from sight into the deep. It was at about 300 or more feet deep before he saw them let go of the LRT. Hovering at 100 feet and looking down, he saw them stop swimming upward. They had both passed out from nitrogen narcosis and, like the LRT, began sinking into the deep sea. Divers breathing compressed air normally cannot venture below about 250 feet without losing consciousness from nitrogen narcosis. Ricky watched in horror, knowing he could do nothing to save them. The submarine went down to search but never located their bodies.

After the accident, Lloyds of London tripled the cost of liability insurance for the operation. The expense eventually put Maui Divers out of the diving business.

Rewards and Perils

Only a small amount of pink coral is harvested in Hawai'i today. Most of the raw and finished (cut and polished) pink and red coral sold in Hawai'i is imported from Japan and Taiwan. Ironically, some of the imports are harvested by foreign fishermen from the flanks of old Hawaiian seamounts north of Midway Island but situated in international waters. By origin it is Hawaiian coral.

Black coral continues to be harvested by independent local divers who supply Maui Divers and other local jewelry companies with raw material. Black coral was designated the official gem of the State of Hawai'i in 1987. Part of my job at the University of Hawai'i over the years has been to monitor the health of the local black-coral beds.

Our research program at the university has been faced with the same perils that affected the *Star II* operation, as well as the black-coral divers. I described earlier the last dive of Jose Angel—how he drowned diving for black coral. There have been many other stories like Jose's over the years of lost black-coral divers: Danson Nakaima, Larry Windley, Tim Lebalaster, and Tim's son, Beau, to mention a few. But perhaps the most amazing black-coral story of all is about a man who passed out at 210 feet, was brought to the surface unconscious, and lived to tell about it.

It was about 1985 and I was conducting my annual survey of the health of the black-coral beds off Lahaina, Maui. I had invited Dennis Pesch, Bret Baxley, and Ricky Ryan to accompany me that day. The plan was to dive the deep reefs about 200 feet down near the old drop-off at Stone Wall, where Jack Ackerman discovered black coral in 1958. We landed at 210 feet. Ricky had agreed to help me count and measure black-coral trees along a 100-meter transect; Dennis and Bret were going to collect a couple of trees. By the end of the dive, Ricky and I were about 100 feet ahead of Bret and Dennis. As we inflated our flotation bags with exhaled air, to aid with the long ascent to the surface, I looked back toward Bret and saw him struggling to tie up his coral trees. I couldn't see Dennis. In several seconds, Ricky and I began rising fast, holding on securely to our buoyant lift bags. At about 150 feet from the surface, I looked back and saw Bret push off the bottom, his float bag bursting with air, heading fast for the surface. Dennis looked like he was holding on to Bret's legs. In less than a minute all four of us had reached the first decompression stop at 20 feet. Ricky and I let go of our lift bags, slowing to a complete stop. Glancing over at Bret and Dennis, I could see they had caught up with us. Their bodies were cloaked in a massive hail of bubbles, like a runaway torpedo, and kept right on going full speed toward the surface.

Cutting short my decompression, I too surfaced to discover what had happened. Dennis had passed out on the bottom. Instinctively, Bret had grabbed Dennis' regulator hose as he pushed off the bottom. Somehow, with superhuman strength, he had managed to hold on to his lift bag with one hand and Dennis with the other. Bret had pulled 200 pounds of dead weight through 200 feet of water at an amazing speed of about 15 mph. On the bottom, Dennis had inhaled so much water that there was little air left in his lungs to expand. Otherwise, without breathing during the ascent, his lungs would have exploded from the expansion of air. At 200 feet, the pressure is about six atmospheres, therefore a lungful of air taken there would expand to six times the volume at the surface. Dennis would have died of a massive air embolism. As soon as Dennis and Bret hit the surface, the boat was on the spot. The crew pulled Dennis aboard and instantly gave him CPR, pumping his lungs free of water. They also dumped an ice chest of cold water on his head. Sputtering and coughing, Dennis came to. In one more minute, the crew had a new tank and regulator on Dennis and put him back in the ocean. Bret and I, too, with fresh tanks of air, went back down with Dennis to decompress. We went to 80 feet and then slowly began a sixty-minute ascent. It was one of the most anxiety-filled hours of our lives, not knowing whether we would get the bends. Fortunately, the decompression was sufficient to purge our bodies

*Bob Baxley, Bret's dad,
harvesting black coral
at 210 feet off Maui*

of residual nitrogen and any bubbles that had formed during our rapid ascent. That night we all drank two toasts: to Dennis and his good health, and to Bret Baxley, who had miraculously saved his life.

Roger Revelle had promised at Scripps that oceanography would be fun, but I never imagined anything like this. Over several years of diving with SCUBA and in submarines, the adventures have been many. Boh Bartko and I once were stuck under a telephone cable at 1,200 feet for about an hour before the current changed direction and pulled us free. Another day, we were lost on the surface, marooned in the submarine for five hours before the mother ship finally picked up our radio signal. During it all, the good times and the scary, new questions were constantly arising from our observations: What was the history of Hawai'i's deep channels? What determined the speed and direction of the ocean currents, and the geology of the bottom surfaces? Why were precious corals found only in zones of extra-strong bottom current? We mapped seamounts, as well as their coral and manganese crust deposits. How old were the seamounts? Where did they originate—were they part of the original Hawaiian chain of volcanoes? An encore to the romance of studying precious corals, these questions were a new intellectual lure for the future. They led to my study of Lō'ihi Seamount and the origin of the Hawaiian Islands.

A cut-away view of the earth showing the Hawaiian Archipelago and the underlying hotspot anchored in the mantle of the earth. The hotspot is fixed, while the overlying crust of the earth (the Pacific Plate) is slowly moving to the northwest. Each island forms over the hotspot, then is transported to the northwest on the plate, taking its place in the long trail of volcanoes that make up the island chain. Art by Richard Rhoads.

Evolution of Hawaiian-Emperor Chain

11 LŌ'IHI SEAMOUNT AND THE ORIGIN OF THE HAWAIIAN ISLANDS

At the time when the earth became hot
At the time when the heavens turned about
The slime, this was the source of the earth
The source of the darkness that made darkness
Born was the coral polyp, born was the coral, came forth
Born was the long-one (Lō'ihi), living at sea
Guarded by the long-torch, living on land
Darkness slips into light, spreading here, spreading there
Propping up earth, holding up the sky.

Verses from the HAWAIIAN CREATION CHANT *Kumulipo*

Lō'ihi Seamount is an active undersea volcano almost 3,000 feet deep situated about 20 miles east of the Big Island of Hawai'i. I became interested in Lō'ihi for two reasons. Initially, it was new ground to explore for deepwater precious corals. Later on, though, and more important, I got involved in its study because one day it will become the next Hawaiian Island. This means that Lō'ihi is undergoing the same history as every other island in the Hawaiian chain. Lō'ihi is presently in the earliest stage of island formation—a phase in the dramatic life cycle that every other island in the Hawaiian chain has already passed through. To better understand this, let's back up and look at how the Hawaiian Islands were created.

The Hawaiian Islands consist of about one hundred major volcanoes. Most people think of Hawai'i as only eight major islands—Hawai'i, Maui, Kaho'olawe, Lāna'i, Moloka'i, O'ahu, Kaua'i, and Ni'ihau—but they are only the highest islands, in the southeast. Northwest of Ni'ihau is a long chain of leeward islands that include Nihoa, Necker, French Frigate Shoals, Gardner, Laysan, Lisianski, Pearl and Hermes Reef, and Midway and Kure Atolls, along with several large reefs, banks, and seamounts in between. Beyond Midway Atoll, a long chain of seamounts, called the Emperor Seamounts, extends 2,500 miles to the northwest all the way to Kamchatka in Russia. Most of these volcanoes are now drowned islands that began their history in exactly the same place as Lō'ihi: over the Hawaiian hotspot, millions of years ago.

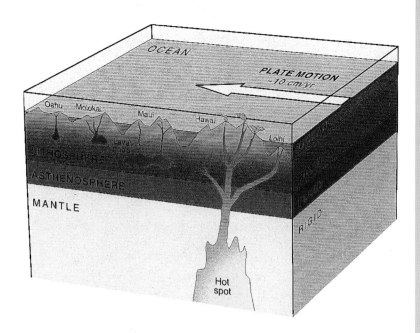

Island formation over the Hawaiian hotspot. The hotspot is fixed in the earth's mantle while slow drift of the lithosphere (earth's crust) to the northwest carries islands off the hotspot and forms a trail of islands (Hawai'i, Maui, Moloka'i, etc.). Once the connection with the hotspot is broken, further vulcanism is limited to lava supplied by a small residual pool beneath each island. Small eruptions from this source of lava on O'ahu are the source of Diamond Head and Punchbowl craters.

Lō'ihi volcano shares a common origin with the other Hawaiian Islands, unique in size and shape but nonetheless a child of the same family. All were created at the same latitude and longitude. We know this because we can measure the original latitude in the lava rocks at the place where they hardened (froze). When molten lavas congeal, the iron compounds that are present in the rock line up with the magnetic field of the earth and are locked in position, forever preserving the geographic latitude of their birth. O'ahu, for example, now situated at 24 degrees north latitude, has lavas that contain a palaeolatitude (ancient latitude) of 19.5 degrees north. Similarly, Midway Island, which has drifted northwest to a latitude of 29 degrees north, has a palaeolatitude in its basement lavas that is also 19.5 degrees north.

The last "island" in the Hawaiian-Emperor Chain (Meiji) is actually a long-drowned volcano. It is now situated at 69.5 degrees north in the far northwestern corner of the Pacific Ocean, more than 4,000 miles from its place of origin over the Hawaiian hotspot. The journey took about 70 million years at a near constant rate of 10 cm/year (about 4 inches/year). The Pacific Plate, on which Meiji was transported, is now sliding under (subducting) the Asian continent. This process has produced a deep

THE HAWAIIAN HOTSPOT

The Hawaiian hotspot is the source of all Hawaiian Islands. It is a stationary plume of lava that extends into the interior (mantle) of the earth almost 700 miles deep. From this upwelling source of fiery rock situated at 19.5 degrees north latitude in the Pacific Ocean, all the Hawaiian Islands were born. The process works as follows. The hotspot heats and thins the overlying crust, leading to a "tree" of upthrusting fractures. Through these conduits volcanoes break out on the seafloor and begin building into new islands. During this process of island formation, the crust of the earth, also known as the Pacific Plate, is gradually moving to the northwest. The crust of the earth is a patchwork of about twenty-five plates, all slowly moving in a process sometimes referred to as plate tectonics or continental drift. Thus, after the formation of each island, the seafloor gradually carries it off the hotspot to the northwest. The connection with the fixed hotspot plumbing is stretched and finally severed. The hotspot then redirects vertically and begins anew to heat and fracture a fresh site for the next volcano. In this way, a chain of islands gradually develops. This process has been going on for at least 70 million years and has produced a trail of about one hundred volcanoes to the northwest, each older than the last, extending 4,000 miles across the Pacific Ocean.

Entering the Alvin *submersible before launching for a 6,000-foot dive to Lōʻihi volcano. Lōʻihi may reach the surface in 50,000 years, when it will become the next Hawaiian Island. Dave Karl photo.*

trench abutting Kamchatka. In several more million years, Meiji will be swallowed up into the trench and finally into the earth's mantle. This history will be the fate of every Hawaiian island unless the Pacific Plate for some reason grinds to a stop, which is unlikely. The hotspot could die, but the plates most certainly will keep on moving. They are driven by a process of constant renewal along edges of formation called *spreading centers.* The spreading center for the Pacific Plate is like a giant zipper, running across the entire eastern Pacific Ocean from south of Australia curving up along South and Central America, finally running aground in the Gulf of California, where it continues landward in the form of the San Andreas fault. All along the plate boundary, new crust is constantly being formed, pushing laterally at right angles to the axis of spreading. It is one of the driving forces of plate tectonics. The other force is slab pull. This takes place when plates subduct, their cold, dense margins pulling them below lighter abutting sections of earth crust.

Formation and destruction of oceanic plates is like a huge conveyor belt. The earth is restless. New crust is constantly emerging, old crust constantly submerging. It's all driven by the push and pull of massive convection cells in the mantle of the earth. The Hawaiian hotspot is situated near the middle of the Pacific Plate. Its islands form, one after the other, as the plate slowly passes overhead.

It is now Lōʻihi's turn. For the past several thousand years, the new island has been slowly building. It rises 12,500 feet off the bottom but still has 3,000 more feet to go before breaking the surface. Instruments called

"seismometers" located at high elevation on the Big Island record earthquake swarms and possible eruptions on Lōʻihi about once every ten years. For every foot added, though, almost as much may be lost to small-scale landslides.

My first dive to Lōʻihi was on February 15, 1987, in the *Alvin* submarine with Dr. Alexander Malahoff. Alex Malahoff is a marine geologist, and a colleague in the Department of Oceanography at the University of Hawaiʻi. Our mission that day was to investigate the processes by which the volcano was growing and to study its biology. Our dive to the bottom lasted seven hours. The first twenty-five minutes were spent sinking 3,200 feet. It was eerie to watch the light slowly dim, gradually turning day into night. At 600 feet, you could still barely read by natural light coming through the ports of the submarine. By 1,000 feet, it was pitch dark and we began to see luminous (bioluminescent) plankton darting here and there. It slowly grew colder and damper. Every now and then, we heard a creak or a small squeak, signifying the increasing pressure on our hull and instruments. We conversed a little to relieve the anxiety but were mainly absorbed by what was passing before our eyes outside. The submarine was under the control of our pilot, Terry Kerby, who handled all navigation and communication with the mother ship topside. As we neared the bottom, a miniature volcanic cone gradually came into view before us, faintly illuminated in the glow of *Alvin*'s reflected light. As Terry adjusted our tiny craft for buoyancy and trim, Malahoff and I scanned the area around us. Suddenly, a plume of water enveloped the submarine. The outside temperature began to jump, from 2.8 to 5 degrees centigrade, then to 10 degrees, then it momentarily zoomed to 25 degrees

The summit of Lōʻihi looks like the surface of another planet. Small chimneys mark the places where hydrothermal fluids leak from the summit. Gary McMurtry photo.

(77 degrees Fahrenheit). We had discovered a small field of hydrothermal vents, all spewing fountains of hot water into an otherwise cold and lightless sea. Bubbles of shimmering water streamed past our ports. We quickly realized the importance of not getting too close to the vents—at 100 degrees centigrade the ports of the submarine would begin to melt. Later in our expedition, another team of scientists would name this place Pele's Vents. Together, we discovered the vent temperatures were 50 degrees Fahrenheit higher than the surrounding ocean (88° F vs. 38° F). The plume water was supercharged with carbon dioxide, 140 times more concentrated than normal. The concentration of methane was 1,000 times above normal and dissolved iron was 20,000 times higher than ambient seawater. The only organisms living in the area of the vents were exotic bacteria so abundant they had formed a thick mat over the landscape.

Peering out into this primordial place, what we saw was an eerie, almost ominous, sight. It seemed as if our submarine had somehow been transported to another planet. Boulders and crags of lava were covered with a Jovian blanket of orangelike snow. We later learned that it was bacteria. The snowlike appearance was because of a constant rain of particles that were blobs of bacteria wafted up in the rising vent water and then, ever so slowly, settling back to the bottom. Here and there we saw a dead shrimp or a crab carcass; only the bacteria were alive. The environment in Pele's Vents was toxic to everything else.

From the summit vent field, Alex and I descended slowly along the north ridge of the volcano. Our six-hour trek covered almost 3 miles of terrain. The most striking discovery we made was the extent to which Lōʻihi Volcano is draped in talus rubble. Apparently, the eruptions along the summit are shallow enough to constantly undergo fragmentation. As pillows of lava break out on the ocean floor, they produce mountains of barrel-sized blocks. Instant cooling splits and cracks the boulders further into a jumble of irregular rubble. In some areas, we saw steep cones of rubble, but more often the landscape looked like the aftermath of a huge landslide. Massive sheets of boulders spread out in all directions from the ridgeline. We calculated the mass of rock wasted downslope was about 90 percent of that produced along the summit rift. Lōʻihi appeared to be losing ground almost as fast as it was being produced.

At 4,000 feet, we finally began to see intact pillow lava flows. The lava fields were no longer fragmented but looked rounded, smooth, layer upon layer, almost like pancakes, densely packed and stable. The only talus we saw below this depth was in steep areas exposed to landslides originating in shallower water. It appeared that we had reached the depth of stability on which the future of the young volcano would depend.

Our observations on this and many other dives to Lōʻihi would later combine with other research on undersea landslides to produce a better

understanding of island history after formation over the hotspot. As plate motion carries the islands off the hotspot, they slowly subside (sink) and erode. Sinking in part is caused by the cooling of the underlying crust as it moves away from the hotspot. Sinking also results from downward deformation of the plate because of the gravitational load of each island. During these transformations, and as the islands move northwestward, they all experience significant losses in mass from huge nearshore or offshore landslides. Abundant evidence of such slides has been found in deep water off virtually all the Hawaiian Islands; however, their occurrence is extremely infrequent. The last major slide off the Big Island is estimated to have taken place about 105,000 years ago off the Kona (south) coast. The wake of this slide has been traced into deep water extending seaward for almost 20 miles. It is calculated to have produced a tsunami of almost 100 meters (more than 300 feet high) that hit Lāna'i. Should another slide and tsunami of this magnitude occur in Hawai'i, the destruction to shoreline property and the potential for loss of life would be enormous. The significance of landslides of this magnitude is that they may well be responsible for some of the most scenic landforms in Hawai'i. For example, the steep cliffing of the eastern side of the Ko'olau Mountains on O'ahu, the so-called Nu'uanu Pali, is thought to be a result of large-scale land collapse producing a massive undersea landslide.

While a great deal more research is needed on giant landslides before they are completely understood, two causal factors appear to be particu-

Hot lava fragments almost instantly into talus blocks, giving way to unstable formations and frequent landslides.

114

larly relevant. One is the degree of instability in the foundations that underlie the land mass lost in the slides. The other, of course, is the trigger. We now surmise that the formation of talus fields during undersea eruptions in the early life of the volcano are the source of instability and are responsible for landslides that may occur at a much later date. As for the trigger, earthquakes are a likely candidate, as time likely will tell.

For the question of when Lōʻihi is expected to reach the surface, we can only speculate. Mauna Loa, on the Big Island, is the largest mountain on earth, rising some 33,000 feet above its base on the ocean floor. Its estimated age is 500,000 years, giving it a rate of accretion of only 0.066 feet per year. At that rate, Lōʻihi would surface in about 50,000 years, give or take. As my friends always say, it is not something to worry about. And as I always remind them, it is something to think about.

Regarding my other research objective, the search for precious coral, Lōʻihi was not very exciting. The environment near the summit is too toxic to support coral growth. It is a highly disturbed place, subject to frequent eruptions and small-scale landslides. The hydrothermal fluids that leak from many surfaces further inhibit marine life. Their high concentration of carbon dioxide produces an acidlike corrosion that kills almost everything but heat-tolerant bacteria. For deepwater coral communities, I would have to look elsewhere. The older islands to the northwest are more promising. Having passed through the early violent stages of island formation, their flanks are stable and swept clean by fresh ocean water far from the influence of volcanoes. In the next chapter, I describe my research at the other end of the Hawaiian Islands. For this voyage, we will travel all the way up the island chain to Kamchatka, visiting the northwestern islands, including the drowned seamounts in the Emperor Chain.

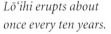

Lōʻihi erupts about once every ten years.

12 THE DARWIN POINT: WHERE HAWAIIAN ISLANDS DROWN

Full fathom five thy father lies;
  Of his bones are coral made;
Those are pearls that were his eyes;
  Nothing of him that doth fade,
But doth suffer a sea-change
Into something rich and strange.

Shakespeare
THE TEMPEST

Coral reefs make waves, as do waves coral reefs. In fact, many if not most of the best surfing spots in the Hawaiian Islands are breaks shaped by coral reefs. Drawn to the sea as I was, it was natural that I would be fascinated by coral reefs. During my early years surfing in Hawai'i, I contemplated the connection between the two, wondering why coral reefs grew in some places and not others. How could coral reefs create such good surfing breaks? How were they formed? How did they affect coastlines overall? What was their history? I often dove the reefs on days when the surf was flat and the water was clear. Everything I saw underwater raised new questions.

During my graduate days at Scripps, I spent three years studying deep, coldwater, sea-fan corals for my Ph.D. dissertation. They were beautiful and fascinating animals. Among other things, I noticed that their growth (branching) was always at right angles to the current. Their fanlike branches served to filter the water for food, the same way a spider's web traps food from the air on land. Because of their predictable growth, sea fans could be used as naturally occurring current meters.

In a more poetic sense, sea-fan corals always sway to the push and pull of overhead waves: To watch this graceful undersea dance is to sense the ebb and flow of life. Waves are the dominant force controlling their growth and development, their very existence, and I felt an abstract kinship with them, being moved by the same elements.

To this day, deepwater corals hold my fascination. Their home is in the twilight zone in the sea. Their habitat is one of the most beautiful, exquisite, and tranquil places on earth. In the black coral beds off

117

Forty-seven species of reef-building corals are found in Hawai'i. This is only 10 percent of the number found in the tropical South Pacific.

Most people are attracted to corals for their exquisite beauty and delicate complexity. Coral reefs represent one of the most diverse ecosystems on earth. A single reef may support several hundred species of coral, five hundred species of fish, and ten thousand species of invertebrates, algae, and bacteria. The food chain within a reef is exceedingly complex. Algae are the primary producers: Their biomass ultimately supports the entire community above them with food. First in line are the herbivores, then the primary, secondary, and tertiary carnivores. In Third World countries, shoreline villagers derive most of their protein from coral reef organisms. A coral reef is a city under the sea teeming with life in an ongoing struggle for survival.

Besides food, coral reefs are important for the massive reefs they build of calcium carbonate (limestone). The coral animal itself is but a thin veneer of living tissue made up of tiny anemone-like polyps joined together into a colony. The colony slowly grows upward by steadily secreting an underlying basement or foundation of limestone. The limestone is like the bones of higher animals. The skeleton supports the living surface of the reef while it slowly accumulates in thickness, layer by layer, reaching ever upward to the surface. The depth at which maximum coral growth takes place in Hawai'i is about 40 to 60 feet, although it varies with the clarity and temperature of the water. The habitat of coral reefs is thus closely

Lahaina, Maui, at a depth of 200 feet, it is so clear that you can look up and see the surface. From there, the sun looks like a twinkling ball in a chandelier of light. Shafts of oblique sunlight penetrate into the crystal blue of the deep. Occasionally, you hear the groan and squeak of a humpback whale passing nearby. The light reaching this depth is about 1 percent of surface intensity. It is enough to read the numbered tags on my research experiments with black corals but not enough for the true reef-building species to thrive. The optimum depth for reef corals is more on the order of 30 to 90 feet (about 10 to 30 meters).

In contrast to such deepwater corals as black and pink coral, reef-building species occur in shallow water and all contain tiny, single-celled plants (algae called "zooxanthellae") in their tissues. These plants require energy from the sun to carry out photosynthesis. While the reef corals provide a safe home to the algae, they in turn manufacture simple compounds that are shared with the coral for food, a symbiotic interaction between coral and algae.

Darwin's Theory of Atoll Development

This brings me to the subject of this chapter, a project called The Darwin Point study. Charles Darwin, of course, is most famous for his discovery of natural selection and evolution. During his famous trip around the world in the ship *Beagle*, however, Darwin conceived an equally famous theory on the origin of coral atolls (islands built entirely of coral encircling a lagoon). Darwin knew that corals grow only in shallow water or to several hundred feet deep. He pondered how islands built entirely of coral could seemingly rise up from the deep sea. Hundreds of coral islands had been charted in the open Pacific Ocean by navigators who preceded Darwin's 1836 voyage. Many of the coral islands were atolls in which a string of connected tiny islets encircled lagoons. Was it possible that all of these islands grew up from shallow banks that just happened to be situated within 200 feet or less of the surface? Darwin dismissed this possibility as unlikely.

In Tahiti on April 12, 1836, Darwin conceived a more plausible answer. He had hiked up the slopes behind Point Venus, where he sat at about 1,000 feet above sea level and looked down. What he saw was a barrier reef encircling Tahiti, as well as one around Moorea, 18 miles distant. The encircling reefs looked like they were growing up from water too deep to support the growth of corals. In his mind's eye, Darwin surmised that both islands must be slowly sinking. As the islands sank, the reefs continued to grow upward, keeping pace with the surface. If a volcanic island were to completely sink below the surface (such as the one he was standing on), the outer reef would be the only thing remaining at the surface. In its place would be a lagoon. An atoll would have been born.

Darwin's theory of atoll development was in question for more than

tied to the surface of the ocean. If sea level were to rise, coral reefs would continue to grow upward, trying to keep pace. Conversely, if sea level were to fall, coral reefs would be stranded high and dry. As creatures of the surface waters, coral reefs are inevitably trapped within a narrow, shallow zone in the tropical oceans under conditions of peak sunlight and optimum water quality.

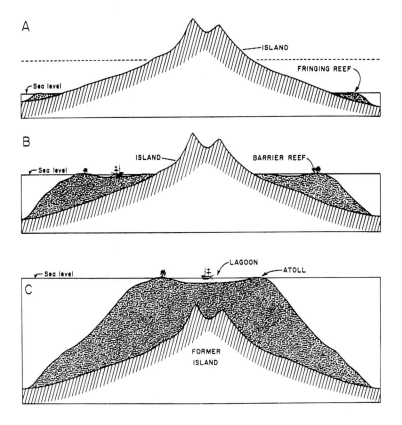

Darwin's theory of atoll development proposed that the upward growth of coral on a sinking volcano gives rise to a circular coral reef, which eventually forms an atoll. After Darwin, 1839.

119

one hundred years. One obvious way to test the theory was to drill to the base of an atoll and determine if indeed it was resting on the top of a long-ago drowned volcano. Such an experiment was conducted by the British on Funafuti Atoll in 1896. They drilled a 1,000-foot hole through solid coral, providing strong evidence that the island had undergone significant subsidence; however, they did not reach a volcanic basement. It was not until 1950, at Enewetak Atoll, that a drill core finally reached the volcanic foundation underlying an island. Two cores consisting entirely of coral were recovered from the drills, one from a depth of 4,222 feet and the other from 4,610 feet. The volcanic rock from the bottom of the core (top of the drowned volcano) was found to be more than 40 million years old. Hence, the coral reef on the top of Enewetak submarine volcano had been growing upward for at least 40 million years. It was a process that Charles Darwin had conceived in an instant.

I had long thought about Darwin's theory of atoll formation in terms of how it might apply to the Hawaiian Islands. In the previous chapter on Lōʻihi submarine volcano, I described the history of the origin of the Hawaiian Islands. The first step in the process is creation over the hotspot, followed by a million or so years of edifice building. After this, movement by plate tectonics transports each island off the hotspot to begin a 70-million-year journey to the northwest. During the long journey, the once high and majestic islands gradually sink and erode. At the same time, coral reefs gradually grow upward and develop protective barriers around the islands. After about 10 million years of subsidence and erosion, most of the islands reach sea level. During that period, plate tectonics carry them about 500 miles to the northwest. Once at sea level, the islands begin the process of atoll development. Coral islets form from accumulated storm deposits that ring the central lagoons.

In the Hawaiian chain today, French Frigate Shoals is an example of an island in the atoll stage of development. A tiny pinnacle of lava rock still protrudes 120 feet above sea level, but otherwise the island is built entirely of coral. Northwest of French Frigate Shoals lie thirteen more coral islands or shallow banks. All are moving to the northwest, and each is progressively older than the previous. The foundations of all of them are slowly sinking, but the coral reefs keep pace with sea level by steadily growing upward. Were it not for coral reefs, in fact, each island would have sunk below the surface of the sea at the point where it reached sea level. All of the islands to the northwest of French Frigate Shoals have survived at sea level for millions of years because of the upward growth of corals.

A question that occurred to me was where and when would the coral stop growing? As the islands moved farther northwest on the plate, they moved into progressively cooler water and latitudes where less average sunlight is available year-round. At some point, moving to higher latitudes, the reefs should die. This point should mark the latitude where the Hawaiian Islands drown. It should coincide with the end of the Hawaiian chain and represent a threshold beyond which atolls could no longer form. I imagined calling such a place the Darwin Point. It would take me about five years to fully test the Darwin Point hypothesis.

Darwin Point Hypothesis

The idea that islands drowned at the northwestern end of the Hawaiian chain came to me one day while diving in the *Star II* submersible at 1,200 feet depth off the west coast of Hawai'i. Boh Bartko and I were surveying a limestone ridge looking for gold coral when I suddenly realized the bottom was actually an old fossil reef. The entire embankment was composed of dead corals. I could even recognize a species of coral *(Porites lobata),* which does not live below 100 feet deep. The island of Hawai'i must have sunk about 1,100 feet since this reef had lived. Death and sinking of the

Islands form over the hotspot and then are carried northwest on the Pacific plate, which is moving about 10 cm/year, while gradually sinking. Once the islands pass a narrow zone of uplift, near O'ahu, slow subsidence resumes and eventually leads to drowning and subduction. The black shading on the islands represents coral growth in zones 1, 2, and 3.

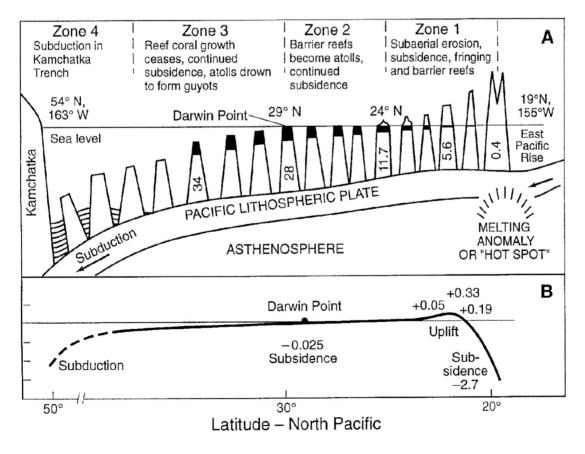

reefs around an island could explain its ultimate drowning. To test this idea, I would have to measure the growth rate of corals and the subsidence rate of all islands across the Hawaiian Archipelago, a distance of 1,400 miles. It would also be important to verify whether drowned coral reefs existed on the tops of submerged banks and seamounts northwest, beyond the farthest Hawaiian island, Kure Atoll.

In 1976 an extraordinary event helped me obtain research funding to test the Darwin Point hypothesis. That year, the United States extended its economic jurisdiction to 200 miles. Suddenly, a pot of money was available for the study of marine resources within the 200-mile zone. The Hawaiian chain was a perfect place for the research. Two hundred miles on either side of a 1,400-mile chain of islands represented 560,000 square miles of U.S. ocean territory. With help from several other scientists at the University of Hawai'i, I put together a five-year research program to study all aspects of marine resources in the Hawaiian chain. The project was called the Northwestern Hawaiian Island Research Investigations (NWHI-RI). It included studies of all the major fisheries in Hawai'i: lobster, shrimp, bottom fish, reef fish, tuna, and other highly migratory species. The entire ecosystem was scrutinized, from algae to invertebrates, including the threatened and endangered species—green turtles and monk seals—and, of course, coral reefs. Coral reefs were my part of the study.

Previous research had determined the rates of subsidence for all islands in the chain. Previous studies also had established that fossil corals were present on drowned seamounts to the northwest of Midway and Kure Islands at the end of the chain. My job, in testing the Darwin Point hypothesis, would be to measure the growth of corals off all the major islands. During the late 1970s, we organized about twenty-five cruises to the northwestern Hawaiian Islands. Ten expeditions were aboard the *Easy Rider,* with captain Skip Neftel. Several other trips were aboard flights to Midway and Kure in C-130 airplanes with the U.S. Coast Guard. Twice yearly, we chartered flights to French Frigate Shoals, where a Fish and Wildlife Research Station greatly facilitated our research. The NWHIRI program was the most intensive period of research in my life. We spent thousands of hours underwater. We dived on every island, islet, bank, and shoal in the Hawaiian Islands. It was the first—and probably last— opportunity for all of us to gather data and information on such a vast scale. More than two hundred scientists participated in the study.

The results of the Darwin Point test were remarkably clear. The growth of corals did gradually decrease to the northwest. The primary factors controlling their growth were decreasing temperature and sunlight. An unexpected finding was a gradual increase in sea urchin predation and erosion on the reefs as we progressed northwest into cooler water. On

Kure Atoll, the last island in the chain, the very slow rate of upward coral growth was almost exactly balanced by the losses in coral limestone from urchin erosion. The sinking rate at Kure was extremely small, but still sufficient to drown an island without active reef building. The threshold for atoll drowning was primarily controlled by biological processes; an equation determined by coral growth gains minus bio-erosional losses. The Darwin Point was confirmed. Hawaiian Islands drown because plate motion carries them beyond a latitude where coral reefs can maintain themselves at sea level.

The Darwin Point experiment answered many questions that had originally attracted me to study coral reefs. We now understand much better the natural forces that regulate the growth of coral reefs. From this basic knowledge, the potential effects on coral reefs of pollution (dredging, sewage disposal, or nonpoint source run-off from the land), and other disturbances caused by human activities, can be better evaluated.

My pursuit of the Darwin Point was enormously interesting. Even more rewarding was the simple truth it produced. It is a feeling shared by many scientists. The driving force is curiosity. The reward is a better understanding of the world we live in. I am fortunate to have had the opportunity and freedom to follow these basic instincts.

The history of the Hawaiian Archipelago and Islands, from birth to drowning to burial (subduction), is a process that takes about 70 million years. From "Islands," Weldon Owen Publishing, Australia.

Palmyra Lagoon, near the site where
Muff Graham's bones were found

13 MURDER ON PALMYRA ISLAND

Double, double toil and trouble;
Fire burn and cauldron bubble.

Shakespeare
MACBETH

Oceanography is the study of the sea and all its phenomena. As an ocean-ographer, I am sometimes retained in law cases dealing with civil or criminal complaints associated with the ocean. The most interesting and by far the most celebrated case I ever worked on was the infamous double murder on Palmyra Island in August 1974. The victims were Muff (Eleanor) and Mac Graham. Buck Walker and Stephanie Sterns were charged with the murders. Both couples had sailed to Palmyra Island that summer, Walker and Sterns to escape legal probation in Hawaiʻi, and the Grahams to begin a round-the-world dream sail. Unfortunately for the Grahams, both couples arrived on Palmyra at the same time.

I was sitting in my office at the University of Hawaiʻi in the spring of 1983 when the telephone rang. Earle Partington, the court-appointed public defender for Buck Walker, wanted to know if I would be interested in being part of a team that would seek to verify Buck Walker's story of what had happened to Muff and Mac Graham on Palmyra Island almost ten years earlier. Like most people in Honolulu, I was somewhat familiar with the facts of the case. The two couples, Mac and Muff Graham and Buck Walker and Stephanie Sterns, had been in Palmyra at the same time for a month or two. Except for them, Palmyra was uninhabited. There had been trouble between them. Walker and Sterns were running out of food. The Grahams were well supplied for a two-year cruise around the world. Walker's boat was leaking and in bad repair. The Grahams' yacht, *Sea Wind,* was in tip-top condition. Walker had been awaiting sentencing on drug charges in Hawaiʻi when he and Sterns had fled by sailing south from Maui in early June 1974. They reached Palmyra in twenty days, a sail that normally takes about seven days. They barely knew how to sail, much less navigate, their 31-foot sloop, *Iola.* Buck and Stephanie's "discovery" of Palmyra was miraculous, if not a complete accident.

Mac and Muff (Eleanor) Graham aboard their yacht, Sea Wind. *Photo courtesy of Earle Partington.*

125

In Earle Partington's phone call, he explained that we would have to sail to Palmyra from Honolulu because the runway there was no longer functional, having been reclaimed by an overgrowth of vegetation. The last plane that had attempted to land there had crashed. Our trip would take seven days under sail. We would be on Palmyra five days, then sail to Christmas Island, two days away, where several of us could fly home. The whole trip would take about two weeks. It was scheduled for late August 1984, to coincide with the time of year when the murders occurred. I would have to take two weeks' vacation, but it wouldn't interfere with classes at the university. Even before Earle finished talking, I had decided to go.

Earle Partington, defense attorney for Buck Walker, claims no one will ever know exactly what happened on Palmyra Island on August 30, 1974, when Muff and Mac disappeared. Was it murder? If not, what did happen to Muff and Mac Graham? Did Buck Walker force Mac to "walk the plank?" If not, how did Mac die and where is his body? Could Mac and Muff, as Buck Walker claims, really have overturned in their Zodiac and drowned in Palmyra Lagoon? Why, then, were all of Muff Graham's bones found clustered together in the sand on the inner rim of the island lagoon? How long did her bones lie there on the beach, unknown and unseen by human eyes? How and when did the grease ants invade her bones? And what of the empty metal box found tangled in the *naupaka* and mangrove roots next to her bones? Why was the inner lining of the metal box scorched and caked with a waxy substance? Had there been a second metal box? Did Stephanie Sterns know the answers to these questions or was she an innocent bystander to one of the most heinous crimes of our century? Buck Walker knows what happened, but he isn't talking. To this day, Walker maintains his innocence, but his account of the story did not hold up to scientific scrutiny.

On August 30, 1984, exactly ten years to the day after the disappearance of the Grahams, our team of two oceanographers and two lawyers revisited Palmyra Island. Our job was to search for clues and to discover what had happened to the Grahams. It was a job that led to surprising results, and despite four trials in the intervening years (two for theft of the Graham's yacht and two for murder), part of the story still has never been told. Even more intriguing, part of the story is still a mystery.

In 1976, Buck Walker and Stephanie Sterns had been convicted of stealing the *Sea Wind* on Palmyra Island. They had sailed it back to Honolulu after Muff and Mac Graham disappeared. The *Iola* had deteriorated so much that Buck towed it out of Palmyra Lagoon to deep water beyond the reef and simply let it sink to a watery grave. On the return trip to Hawai'i, Buck and Stephanie renamed the *Sea Wind* and tried to disguise her with a new paint job. His first day back in port in Honolulu,

MEMORIES OF PALMYRA

I had been to Palmyra Island twenty-three years earlier, in 1961, when I was a graduate student at the University of Hawai'i in the Department of Zoology. Dr. Albert Banner had been studying ciguatera, the so-called fish poison or toxin found in the flesh of some tropical reef fishes. Palmyra, for some unknown reason, is a region where many of the reef fish are poisonous. Banner had arranged an expedition to the island over Christmas break and invited some graduate students to go with him and help collect poisonous fish. We flew down from Honolulu in a military cargo plane and landed on the runway built by the Army Corps of Engineers just before World War II. The runway was already beginning to crack because of encroaching weeds and vegetation. The island seemed to me a vaguely eerie place. The U.S. Navy and Marines had occupied Palmyra during the war. About five thousand troops had been stationed there during the peak action of the Pacific war against the Japanese. A large number of barracks, workshops, and other buildings were still there, unoccupied, barren, and desolate. It rains about 200 inches a year on Palmyra, and in the sixteen years since the war, many of the wooden buildings had begun to rot. Walking around in them was dangerous because of the rotting floorboards, walls, and ceilings. On New Year's Eve, 1961, we set fire to a rotted barracks annex that had almost completely collapsed. It burst into flames, which leaped upward

Buck Walker actually reregistered the *Sea Wind* under a new name, *Lōkahi*. He claimed on the registration form to have recently finished building it. Several days later, in the Ala Wai Boat Harbor, friends of the Grahams recognized the vessel as the original *Sea Wind* and reported it. The police closed in on Buck and Stephanie, hoping to nab them red-handed aboard the stolen yacht. Buck was tipped off, though, and managed to escape by diving overboard and swimming underwater, coming up for air between moored boats. Buck had escaped, but not for long. Ten days later he was apprehended, holed up in a cheap hotel in Hāwī on the Big Island.

In the sensational trial that followed in August 1975, Buck Walker and Stephanie Sterns were found guilty on all counts—stealing the *Sea Wind*, stealing $400 from the boat, and transporting stolen goods in interstate commerce. Buck Walker was sentenced by Judge Samuel P. King to ten years in a federal penitentiary, to commence after he had first served a previous five-year sentence on drug charges. Stephanie was sentenced to two years in federal prison, with five years' probation.

Buck Walker served almost four years of his sentence at the federal penitentiary at McNeil Island in Puget Sound, Washington, before escaping in 1979, only to be caught and re-arrested on August 13, 1981, in Yuma, Arizona, on a fugitive warrant. This time, Walker was sent to a high-security prison, in Marion, Illinois. Stephanie served seven months of her sentence at Terminal Island Federal Correctional Institution off Long Beach, California, followed by ninety days in a Santa Barbara halfway house before being released in February 1978, having then been judged to have paid her debt to society.

Then, almost three years later, on January 25, 1981, one of the missing bodies was discovered on Palmyra Island. Sharon Jordan had taken a morning stroll along the beach on the inner lagoon of Strawn Islet. Sharon and her husband, Robert, had been on Palmyra for several months, resting up before resuming their round-the-world ocean voyage. Sharon had been shell collecting when something shiny in the sand caught her eye. Bending down to pick it up, she suddenly recognized it as a gold crown in a human jaw. Instantly, the story of the missing couple shot through her mind. She recoiled in horror and, looking around, saw the rest of the skeleton scattered in the sand. All the bones were clustered within a small circle perhaps 10 feet in diameter. A tangled mangrove grew a few feet up the beach, and under the mangrove lay a heavily corroded metal box. Between the bones and the box a lid rested upright on the beach. Inside the lid was one bone and a lady's wristwatch.

On February 4, 1981, a team from the Federal Bureau of Investigation left Honolulu for Palmyra Island. After six days, they returned with the skeleton, the box, various photographs, and pieces of evidence collected

We searched the whole island for Mac Graham

70 feet high. We stood in the dark of night celebrating the arrival of the new year. As the barracks slowly crumbled into embers and ash, the stars in the tropical sky were more brilliant than I had ever seen them.

at the scene. A week later the skull and bones were identified as those of Eleanor "Muff" Graham, by a forensic odontologist using dental charts obtained from Muff's dentist in San Diego. Three days later a federal grand jury in Honolulu indicted Buck Walker and Stephanie Sterns for murder in the first degree.

Again the wheels of justice began to turn. In the following four years, both Walker and Sterns were brought to trial, though separately. On March 12, 1982, U.S. District Court Judge James M. Burns followed the protocol established for the theft trials in 1975 and severed Buck Walker's case from that of Stephanie Sterns.

The outcome of both cases is history. Walker was convicted of first-degree murder in June 1985. His story, that Mac and Muff Graham had gone fishing on the afternoon of August 30, 1974, and never returned, could not be corroborated by our team of investigators hired to re-create the circumstances of his story. Walker had claimed the Grahams must have overturned in their Zodiac and been eaten by sharks. Walker said the Grahams had gone out to catch dinner for a farewell party for Buck and Stephanie, who allegedly had planned on leaving Palmyra the next day for Fanning Island, where they could replenish their dwindling supply of food. Never mind that Fanning Island lies 175 miles upwind from Palmyra, and without a motor in the *Iola,* sailing there would have been virtually impossible with normal winds. When Mac and Muff failed to return to the *Sea Wind,* Buck and Stephanie had gone aboard to wait for them.

The story of what really may have happened that day has been told in a fascinating book by Vincent Bugliosi, *And the Sea Will Tell,* also portrayed in a mini–TV series by the same name. It took only one hour and twenty-three minutes for the jury to find Buck Walker guilty of murder. Stephanie Sterns was acquitted in a separate trial a year later. Vincent Bugliosi and Leonard Weinglass were successful in presenting her defense. Bugliosi argued that Stephanie never knew what happened on August 30, 1974; Buck had kept her busy onboard the *Iola* all day, baking bread for the never-to-be-held farewell party. Buck had taken the *Iola* dinghy with him to be sure Stephanie did not leave the *Iola.* Meanwhile, he had murdered both Muff and Mac Graham and disposed of their bodies. His means of disposal was to place at least one body into a metal box and dump it in the middle of the lagoon. Walker took the metal box from the hull of an abandoned rescue boat that had washed up on the beach near the *Sea Wind.* This means of disposal was so bizarre that it actually figured strongly in proving Stephanie's innocence. Why would Walker go to such lengths to hide the body if Stephanie was a party to the crime?

What else was there about Buck Walker's story that did not hold up in

SEARCHING FOR CLUES

As part of our investigation, our team placed the carcass of a large fish at the site where Muff's bones were found. Within several hours, thousands of land crabs had crept out of the jungle to feed on the decaying "body." Within two days, the skeleton was stripped clean and the bones and skull (weighing about 4 pounds) had been dragged more than 100 feet down the beach in both directions. Obviously, Muff's bones would have suffered the same fate, had her body washed ashore after a fatal shark attack. Instead, the bleached and corroded bones were all within a tidy 10-foot circle, a fact completely overlooked during the trial.

Further studies proved that the sand on the beach was too thin to have covered her body, thus eliminating the only other possible means that would have protected the bones from scavenging crabs, rats, and wild dogs. This evidence absolutely linked Muff's bones to the metal container, incontrovertible evidence that she was murdered. Another clue passed over in trial was the large number of grease ants found in Muff's bones. During the seven years on the beach concealed in an ever-corroding metal box, grease ants would have had little trouble finding their way inside. Had the box floated in and broke up on the beach after spending seven years on the bottom, deep in the lagoon, where wave activity was nil, the bones would not have been on the beach long enough to have been invaded by the grease ants. Nor would they have

court? The first thing we did was to try and overturn a Zodiac in Palmyra lagoon. The Zodiac we used was the exact same model, with the same size engine as the one owned by the Grahams. No matter how we drove it—slow, fast, turning on a dime, spinning in every possible direction— our test pilot, Bret Baxley, could not overturn it. The weather during our trials was the same as it had been on August 30, 1974: light trade winds with passing squalls, winds up to 15 knots, not even close to what it would have taken to overturn the Zodiac. Yet the Zodiac was found upside-down on the beach. The next morning, when Buck and Stephanie "found" the Zodiac, Buck righted the boat and put it back in the water and started the engine after several cranks. Later, in Honolulu, it would be revealed that not one drop of seawater had been inside the engine. Had the Zodiac floated to the beach upside-down, the engine would have been flooded and it would not have started.

Well, then, perhaps the Grahams simply fell out of the Zodiac? Possibly, but even if they did, Mac was a strong swimmer, and he would have assisted Muff. What about sharks? In seventeen hours of searching under-water for Mac, who could have been disposed of in a second box, Bret Baxley and I saw only one gray reef shark. The blacktip sharks that had been reported to be so abundant by the FBI and others at Palmyra in the summer of 1974 were very small. They rarely grow larger than 2 or 2.5 feet long, and they are not particularly aggressive. During our expedition, in fact, we witnessed the wild dogs on Palmyra herding blacktip sharks into shallow water and chasing them up onto the beach, where they ate them. Blacktips usually reside on the reef flats in water only 1 or 2 feet deep, making them easy prey for the dogs. The blacktips would not nor-mally have been in the middle of the lagoon, nor would they normally have been large or aggressive enough to attack and kill a human being. Also, none of Muff Graham's bones bore any teeth marks, which surely they would have if she had been attacked and killed by sharks.

According to the story of what happened as presented by Elliot Enoki, the prosecuting attorney in both murder trials, Walker had murdered and disposed of Eleanor Graham in the following way. Her jawbone was detached and her molar teeth had been fractured, both indicating severe trauma probably inflicted by a hard sledge-hammer-like blunt object. According to Boyd Stephans, chief medical examiner and coroner for the City and County of San Francisco, the skull had been exposed to extreme heat, 1,100 degrees Fahrenheit or higher, possibly inflicted by an acetylene torch (which Buck Walker had). The burning was alleged to have taken place while flesh was still on the skull. A hole through the left temple could have been caused by a "contact" gunshot wound. According to the prosecution, Walker had beaten Muff Graham unconscious, shot her at point-blank range, and then dismembered her body and cremated her in

been sun bleached and abraded as the evidence clearly indicated. Muff's bones probably sat on the beach par-tially buried in the sand for months, if not years, exposed to the elements. Even during storms, the waves in the lagoon where the bones were found are very small because of its sheltered location. On this particular beach, the bones would have remained together, as they did.

Land crabs scavenging the carcass of a dead fish as they would have Eleanor Graham's body if, as Walker claimed, it had washed up on the beach.

the metal box. Evidence of fatty acids of possible human origin had been obtained from scrapings taken from inside the box. The inside of the box was scorched, and a fragment of cloth was stuck to the fatty acid deposits. Traces of human blood were detected in the cloth. Though some of this evidence was contradicted by the defense, the prosecution argued that the box had clearly served as a crematorium.

Presumably, Walker had capped the box with a tightly fitting metal lid and wrapped it with wire. He transported the box in the Grahams' Zodiac out into the lagoon and dumped it overboard. Walker then took the Zodiac to a remote point along the inner lagoon about a half mile away from the *Sea Wind,* where he overturned the Zodiac on the beach. He walked back to fetch Stephanie, who meanwhile had been baking bread aboard the *Iola* for the make-believe party Walker had made up. Bugliosi argued that the next day Buck led Stephanie to the overturned Zodiak and allowed her to find it, thus convincing her of his version of the story: that the Grahams went fishing in the Zodiac, overturned, and drowned. But how did the crucial evidence concerning the bones of Eleanor Graham figure in this scenario?

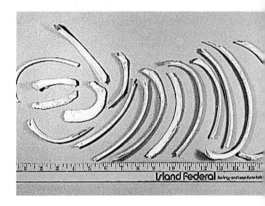

Six years after she was murdered, Muff Graham's skull and bones were discovered at a remote site in Palmyra Lagoon by a lone passerby. Photo courtesy of Earle Partington.

The prosecution claimed that the box containing her bones must have floated up seven years after the murder and drifted ashore, where it broke up and spilled the bones on the beach. They further speculated that the next tide would have washed the bones back into the lagoon, so Sharon's discovery had been no less than an incredible stroke of luck. More likely, the box probably floated to the surface within days of the murder. A decaying corpse normally produces large amounts of methane, hydrogen sulfide, and carbon dioxide gases, which would have caused the box to float within one or two weeks. The box would then have drifted ashore intact. Once on the beach, the body would have completely decayed inside the box, and all remaining flesh would have been removed by bacterial processes. When the box finally corroded open, the bones would have spilled out onto the beach and they would have been clean of all remaining flesh and organic matter. This scenario would explain why the bones were found all together. Had a body that had been attacked and killed by sharks washed up on the beach, the carcass would have been pulled helter-skelter up and down the beach by scavenging animals.

And what about Mac Graham? If in fact Mac suffered the same fate as Muff, his remains should long ago have surfaced. And yet, despite all the considerable searches, including our own, which involved five days of hunting and diving, only one clue has been discovered. In June 1980, another bone was found about 200 yards east of the site of Muff Graham's skeleton, again by a visiting yacht person. Galatea Eatinger said it was probably a humerus bone, definitely human. Not realizing the possible significance of her find, Galatea later tossed the bone back into the lagoon. Whether the bone was indeed human and whether it came from Mac Graham's body may never be known. Only two things can be said about it. First, it wasn't part of Muff's skeleton, because both her humerus bones had been accounted for, and second, the bone is still there. Perhaps the second metal box is, too.

In 1984, we discovered a rescue boat from which the box containing Muff Graham's bones had been taken. It was underwater at a depth of about 15 feet. Later, when I reviewed my underwater photographs of the boat, it was clear that two boxes were missing from it, not just one. Out of four metal containers in the hull of the rescue boat, two boxes were missing. We also later learned from the theft trial transcripts that the rescue boat in August 1974 had been washed up on land next to the *Sea Wind*. Sometime in 1979, some Gilbertese natives had pushed the rescue boat into the lagoon, where it sank. That was where we found it in 1984, minus the two metal boxes. Did Buck Walker make Mac Graham "walk the plank," as he had bragged to a fellow cellmate at McNeil Prison, or did he massacre him like he did Muff and dispose of the body in the second box? The empty hole in the rescue boat, where the second box had been, strongly suggests the second possibility.

So . . . where is the second box? Whoever answers this question will solve the one remaining mystery surrounding the Palmyra murder case. Buck Walker probably knows, but long ago he decided to remain silent. Walker never took the stand in his own defense during his trial, and he steadfastly refused to talk to the prosecuting attorney during the trial of Stephanie Sterns.

Where is Mac Graham? Perhaps no one will ever know, as Earle Partington said in the trial. Or perhaps another passerby will one day stumble over a bone in the sands of Palmyra Lagoon. The site where Galatea Eatinger made her discovery would be a good place to resume the search. Like the Incan treasure of gold and silver aboard the Spanish pirate ship *Esperanza*, which went aground on Palmyra and was buried there in 1816, Mac's whereabouts is just one more question that adds to the haunting aura of Palmyra's mysteries.

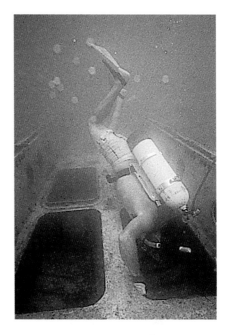

During our diving surveys, Bret Baxley and I discovered a rescue boat on the bottom of the lagoon. The metal box in which Muff Graham was cremated came out of the right forward compartment. Notice the left forward compartment is also missing its metal liner. Was this the second box?

Sunrise on Palmyra Atoll

Ron Church photo

14 THE OCEAN OF TRUTH AND THE ENVIRONMENT

The world was not left to us by our parents. It was lent to us by our children.

African Proverb

Saving the ocean is like motherhood and apple pie. It is something most people want to do, myself included. And there are many serious marine problems in need of attention. Perhaps the biggest problem in the ocean worldwide is overfishing. Overdevelopment of the coastline is another serious issue. It has been estimated that 50 percent of the world's population of 5.8 billion people live within 50 miles of a coast. Oil spills and ocean pollution are other subjects we frequently hear about. But is pollution as serious a problem as it often is portrayed? In this chapter, I discuss environmental problems, particularly as they affect surfers and other ocean recreationists. It is a controversial subject, often highly emotional. It is also a subject where the truth often becomes lost in the shuffle. Surfers and other environmentally concerned people are sometimes manipulated in the process. Having spent over half of my life studying these problems, I would like to offer some thoughts and insights.

Is pollution in the ocean real? Yes, of course it is, but possibly not to the extent we are sometimes led to believe. Many areas of the world are in serious jeopardy. Almost all of them are in regions of urban development. They are generally places where circulation and mixing in the ocean are confined or somehow restricted—embayments, harbors, marinas, inlets, estuaries, and inland coastal waterways. Along the open coastlines, especially in areas exposed to large waves and vigorous mixing, pollution problems are much less significant. In the United States, deepwater ocean sewage outfalls have virtually eliminated problems that once existed. Why then do we continue to hear a hue and cry about the negative effects of sewage outfalls?

There's a lot of propaganda out there. I can cite at least four sources of misinformation from groups that have a vested interest in promoting pollution myths. Fishermen are sometimes very willing offenders. After all, it is much easier to point the finger at pollution for declining fish stocks than to admit that overfishing is to blame. Environmental groups also sometimes find the pollution bandwagon convenient to their cause. Saving the ocean requires there be a villain. A rich corporation or a government agency makes a convenient target. Targets which, incidentally, also have deep pockets and may be profitable to sue. An agenda promoting pollution problems may advance membership drives or fund-raising efforts. It can also enhance visibility or bring about recognition in the press. And the media is rarely interested in good news. When I report results of my research showing that a pollution problem does not exist or is only minor, the media universally is not interested. But when someone claims there is a problem, it makes the nightly television news or the front page of the newspaper, and the media does not always check out its sources. Bad news sells. Finally, there are research scientists who exaggerate problems to get research funding. The bigger the problem, the greater the need for the research. It justifies the budget.

I mention all of this because I believe that the success of the environmental movement ultimately rests on the truth. Trumping up problems will eventually undermine the credibility of our purpose. When Jacques Cousteau used to tell us "The seas are dying," we might have sent in $20 to join his organization, but later when we found out that the seas were not dying, we might have cancelled our membership. All of us who are concerned about the ocean deserve to know the truth.

As a scientist, my job is to discover the truth and then report it. Sometimes I find myself in agreement with environmental groups against a particular issue or project, but not necessarily for the same reasons. For example, take the Lihi-Lani project. Lihi-Lani is a large, suburban development consisting of about three hundred homes proposed for the North Shore of Oʻahu. I am against the project because it exceeds the carrying capacity of the area for traffic and other infrastructure. The North Shore community, too, is against the project, but their argument is that the development will cause run-off and pollution to coral reefs, ruin the surf, and pose a health hazard to surfers. These claims are totally unfounded and so scientifically false, I ended up opposing the North Shore community in public hearings on the project. In their eyes, I was seen as supporting the project, but I was simply reporting the truth. They did not believe the traffic argument was strong enough, so instead they used a false but emotionally powerful argument claiming the project would pollute the ocean.

Another similar situation involved a sewer outfall on the south shore of Oʻahu off ʻEwa Beach. Previous research had demonstrated that the outfall was environmentally sound. Because of its distance offshore (2 miles), depth (240 feet), and sewage treatment (advanced primary), no detrimental effects on marine life could be detected. Therefore, when the Sierra

An environmental myth in Hawaiʻi is that sewer outfalls pollute the ocean. Once true, it is no longer a valid argument, because of modern technology. The fish seem to agree.

Club Legal Defense Fund sued the City and County of Honolulu for $42 million, claiming exactly the opposite, I found myself in court lined up against them. The Sierra Club Legal Defense Fund sued because of technical violations by the City and County, reasoning they could win on that basis. As a result of the lawsuit, the court mandated $9 million for further research, which ultimately proved the City and County had been correct all along. Despite the outcome of the study, I was viewed by many environmentalists as supporting the side of pollution. It is not always easy to stand by the truth.

The ocean is like a second conscience to me. It is a symbol of the truth, and it holds me to it. My message is simply the results of my research—it is what it is, good or bad. As scientists or environmentalists, our message must be honest, otherwise we compromise ourselves in the process of trying to save the very cause we believe in. We self-destruct on false ideals.

In my view, the biggest problem facing humankind is overpopulation. In my lifetime, I've seen the world population triple in size. In fifty more years, it will probably double again. All surfers have an extraordinary understanding of the consequences, because they experience it every day of their surfing life in trying to find an uncrowded wave. Surfers understand the "tragedy of the commons" better than the marine ecologists who work with the concept. Common property shared by all becomes a tragedy when the resource becomes limiting. Like an overloaded boat, with the addition of only one more, it may sink. At that point, everybody loses.

Too many people is the problem. If they are the source of pollution, that too is a problem. As environmentalists, we need to attack the cause, not the symptoms. Overpopulation is ignored by most environmental groups because it is politically incorrect. It challenges religious views and political rights and therefore is pushed to the bottom of the agenda or ranked as low priority. The United States does not have a population policy—except for a few million dollars for foreign aid spent for family planning. That's better than nothing, but not by much.

The time has come to attack the cause of the problem, not just the symptoms. Pogo said, "We have met the enemy and he is us." But comics aside, the time has come to get serious about overpopulation. If we concern ourselves only with pollution, every gain we make will be offset by losses caused by increasing numbers of people. Paul Ehrlich, a world authority on the population problem, has determined that the carrying capacity of the earth is about 3 billion people. Our numbers are approaching 6 billion. No wonder things seem to be going downhill.

As we look to the future, our work is cut out for us. Let's use the truth to face not only how to deal with overpopulation but also to develop a credible scientific basis to curb pollution problems where they exist. Now that's an agenda we can all get behind.

"Whatsoever things are pure, whatsoever things are lovely, if there be any virtue, and if there be any praise, think of these things" (Philippians 4:8).

*Standing on a ledge or even low on
a beach can be dangerous when surf
is high. Peter French photo.*

15 OCEAN AND BEACH SAFETY IN HAWAI'I

If in doubt, don't go out.

Ralph Goto
City and County Lifeguards, Honolulu, Hawai'i

Beach and ocean safety has been part of my life since the early 1950s in Santa Monica, where I was first a junior lifeguard and later a regular beach lifeguard during summer breaks in college. We were constantly training to stay physically fit, as well as to improve our lifesaving skills. For me, this was not only a job, it also fit perfectly with being a better and safer surfer. Though I did not continue in lifeguarding after I moved to the Islands, over the years I have been involved in several administrative jobs responsible for water safety. For a time, I served on a diving safety board at the University of Hawai'i. In the 1970s and '80s, the mayor of Honolulu, Frank Fasi, invited me to serve on his Water Safety Commission, which had the responsibility of developing signs warning of high surf on the North Shore of O'ahu. In the 1990s, I was again appointed to a government task force on beach and ocean safety, this time by Governor Ben Cayetano. Our job has been to improve warning systems, primarily signage at all state and county parks in the Hawaiian Islands. It is with this background and experience that I devote this chapter to beach and ocean safety as it relates to surfing and other water sports.

Shore Hazards

At least 20 million people visit the beaches of O'ahu every year. Beach and ocean recreation is clearly an integral part of the life of visitors and residents alike. Ocean conditions at many beaches in Hawai'i, however, can be extremely dangerous. Over the past ten years, three or more drownings and two hundred or more ambulance-assisted accidents have occurred each year on O'ahu alone. Many of the injuries are to bodysurfers or Boogie Boarders. Neck, spine, and back injuries are the most common of the serious accidents. Surprisingly, about 90 percent of the injuries occur when the surf is 3 feet or less; a deceptively powerful shorebreak in very shallow water is frequently the cause. Small waves may

Shorebreak is the number-one cause of broken necks to swimmers, bodysurfers, and Boogie Boarders in Hawai'i.

appear innocuous, but people are routinely carried perilously "over the falls" and slammed into the bottom. Hawaiian beaches are dangerous because of the open, exposed location of the Islands and the scarcity of wide, offshore protective reefs. Sandy Beach, on Oʻahu, for example, has been described by City and County lifeguards of Honolulu as the "broken neck capitol of the world."

When the surf is big in Hawaiʻi, even people standing near the ocean—never mind close—may be in a life-threatening situation. One day in March 1974 at the Banzai Pipeline, I saw four girls swept off the beach by the uprush from a superset of 30-foot-plus waves. The girls were standing at the top of the beach watching the surf, when suddenly the water raced up the beach and engulfed them. In the next few seconds, they were dragged down the beach and into the ocean by the powerful backwash. They disappeared in foam and turbulence. No one saw them for about eight to ten minutes. Then, about 500 yards down the beach, they were spotted bobbing face down in the whitewater. Four men, including me, charged into the water to attempt their rescue. We managed to get all four to shore but not in time to save them. I administered CPR for forty-five minutes to the girl I had pulled in, but without success.

Surfing Hazards

Surfing accidents also claim the lives of too many victims in Hawaiʻi. In general, surfers are knowledgeable and well trained about ocean dangers. Nevertheless, everyone has to learn, and everyone makes mistakes. For surfers, the shorebreak is not as hazardous as it is for swimmers and bodysurfers because surfers generally ride waves farther offshore in deeper water.

The greatest dangers associated with riding big waves in Hawaiʻi are currents and the waves themselves. Surfers should be fully aware of the location, direction, and speed of currents in each surfing area before they go out. They should be strong swimmers, capable of getting back to shore if they are carried seaward by currents. Currents in the surf zone are usually produced by the waves. The bigger and more frequent the waves, the stronger the currents.

Waves can be treacherous simply because of their size. A big wave can snap a surfboard in half—or break the bones of a surfer. Titus Kinimaka was once hit directly on his leg while standing on his board riding a wave at Waimea Bay. The wave broke his femur (thigh bone) in half, producing a compound fracture. Titus went into shock and could barely swim. Luckily, three of his buddies saw the wave take him down and instantly paddled to his aid, probably saving his life.

Hitting the bottom is another serious danger that all surfers face.

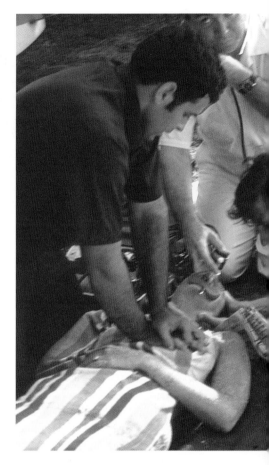

This drowning victim was one of four girls swept off the beach at the Banzai Pipeline during high surf on the North Shore in 1974. The girls were standing too close to the shoreline when a huge set of waves sent a wall of water surging up the beach. It knocked them down and carried them into the sea. Our rescue attempt was too late to save their lives.

Before going out to surf, no matter where, they should know the location and depth of all reefs in the area. Surfers are advised to snorkel or skin dive areas where they surf on days when the waves are calm. Having done this in many areas in Hawai'i, I steadfastly avoid some places, like Pipeline and Backyards at Sunset Beach, because of shallow reefs.

Surfboard cords present another problem. They save surfers a lot of long swims retrieving boards, but they introduce another danger, especially in big surf. Cords can drag a surfer horizontally in the churning whitewater, possibly causing drowning, and they can also become tangled around your leg or arm—or neck—during a wipeout. My cord once became wrapped around my leg at the knee joint, and when it pulled taut, it almost stripped off my calf muscle; my leg was sore for about four months. In waves higher than 15 feet, I do not recommend using a cord.

Safety Measures

Aside from oceangoers acquiring personal knowledge and safety training, a lifeguard is the best safety measure against accidents in the surf. An overall system of beach and water safety is vitally important for the general public. Essential components include the following:

- Lifeguards with adequate training and tools to meet the demands of specific areas.
- Signage conveying specific warnings of the risk, how to avoid the risk, and the consequences of not avoiding the risk. Signage includes beach bulletin boards or chalkboards with information on daily water conditions.
- Zoning areas for special activities.
- Removal of possible hazards, such as logs in the surf.
- Closing the beach to the general public during high surf.
- Warnings of hazards and water safety tips in brochures or videos.

With signage, it helps to establish a testing and evaluation program for existing signs. The results of such tests yield improvements in signage design and placement. Another point to consider for municipalities is standardization of signage. This reduces confusion and enhances public awareness and acceptance.

I hope this chapter will help educate ocean users about some of the dangers of Hawaiian waters, and serve as a wake-up call to those responsible for the management of ocean safety programs. Every individual who uses the ocean in Hawai'i should be aware of its dangers. And finally, I remind you of Ralph Goto's message: "If in doubt, don't go out." It may save your life.

SIGNAGE

Examples of signs developed by the Hawaii Task Force on Beach and Water Safety. The signs convey warnings of a particular risk, how to avoid the risk, and the consequences of not avoiding the risk: a legal minimum standard required by the American National Standards Institute.

WARNING

STRONG CURRENT

YOU COULD BE SWEPT AWAY FROM SHORE AND COULD DROWN

IF IN DOUBT, DON'T GO OUT

WARNING

DANGEROUS SHOREBREAK

WAVES BREAK IN SHALLOW WATER
SERIOUS INJURIES COULD OCCUR, EVEN IN SMALL SURF

IF IN DOUBT, DON'T GO OUT

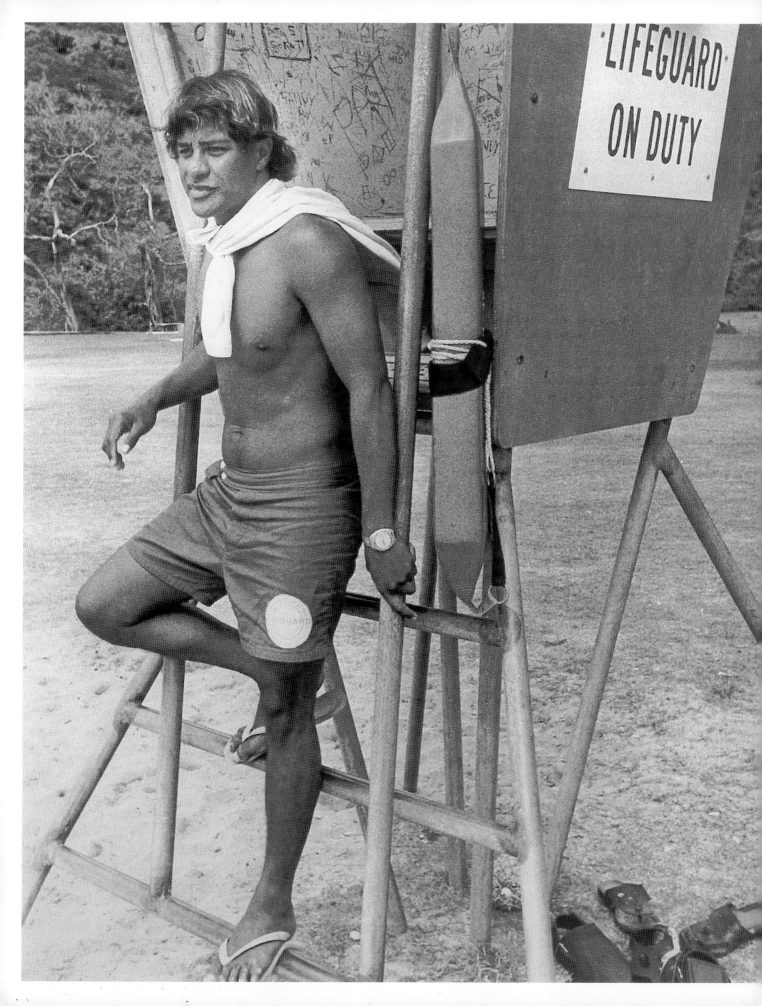

16 EDDIE WOULD GO

The Polynesians were the children of Tangaroa, God of the Sea. They were descendants of Tane, Tu, and Rono, mighty Gods of Nature. Out of filial respect and obedience, they learned to trim their sails, and their lives, in harmony with the natural forces.

Herb Kane
VOYAGE

I got the call at 5:30 in the morning. Peter Cole broke the news to me over the phone. After embarking on its second voyage to Tahiti, the *Hōkūleʻa* had foundered on the first night out somewhere in the Molokaʻi Channel; Eddie Aikau, paddling his surfboard, had gone for help and was missing. Peter asked if I could somehow get a ship and conduct a search. I immediately called Cliff Slater, owner of Maui Divers, to ask if I could borrow their ship *Holokai* for a rescue mission to look for Eddie. Cliff immediately agreed.

Hōkūleʻa *Sets Sail*

Eddie Aikau was well known to everyone in the surfing world, and he was a good friend of mine. Eddie had signed on as crew for the *Hōkūleʻa*, along with fifteen others (fourteen men and one woman), all highly trained, skilled sailors with roots in Polynesia. *Hōkūleʻa* was a 60-foot, twin-hulled Polynesian sailing canoe designed and built to replicate as closely as possible the ancient canoes in which the Polynesians had sailed from Tahiti to Hawaiʻi almost two thousand years ago. For three months the crew had trained on *Hōkūleʻa* in short trips between the Islands. They had experienced wind and waves under the worst conditions possible and *Hōkūleʻa* had held up. This voyage to Tahiti would be the second for *Hōkūleʻa*. The first, in 1976, had been with the aid of an escort boat. It was essentially a test run to see if a Polynesian sailing canoe could succeed in sailing the nearly 2,400 miles, first east against the tradewinds and then south to the Society Islands, where many Polynesian voyages had originated. The maiden trip had been successful, so much so that the second

Eddie Aikau gave his life trying to save the lives of others. It was a noble act by a noble Hawaiian. His name has become legendary in the history of Hawaiʻi. Photo courtesy of the Honolulu Advertiser.

Hōkūleʻa *on the day of departure for its second voyage to Tahiti, March 16, 1978. Photo courtesy of the* Honolulu Advertiser.

voyage would be without escort boat or any modern navigational aids. The purpose was to prove beyond all doubt that Polynesian sailors, ancestors of the Hawaiian race, were indeed the great navigators they were reputed to be. For the crew members, it was also an attempt to reclaim old traditions and old memories, a mission of self-discovery.

The departure date, March 16, 1978, coincided with spring weather, strong trades, and clear skies. Hōkūleʻa's navigator, Nainoa Thompson, would rely for direction finding solely on stars, currents, winds, and waves. Nainoa had studied Polynesian history and trained under the wise tutelage of Mau Piailug, the most acclaimed navigator in all of Polynesia.

On the afternoon set for Hōkūleʻa to leave Honolulu, the trades were blowing hard, 30 to 40 knots in the channels, with higher gusts. Hōkūleʻa had handled similar conditions before, however, and the sailors were confident. Dave Lyman, the captain, had considered waiting a day or two longer, but an elaborate departure ceremony had been planned; dancers, musicians, dignitaries, the governor, the mayor, schoolchildren of Hawaiian descent—the people of Hawaiʻi, twenty thousand strong—were gathered and waiting for the send-off. The departure could not easily be postponed.

Hōkūleʻa left Magic Island on Oʻahu exactly on schedule, at 1900 on Thursday, March 16, 1978, as the setting sun and thousands of cheering friends bid them aloha and godspeed. As soon as the sails were up they were spilling gusts of wind and straining the ropes. The first five hours were like a downhill race, streaming into huge port seas but knifing ahead at 8 knots. Near midnight everything suddenly changed. The starboard hull began taking on water, fast. The sea had heeled Hōkūleʻa over so far that the downwind hull was set too deeply in the water. Lyman issued an order to jettison stores, food, equipment, personal effects—and to start bailing. The crew complied, but it was too late. They simply could not bail fast enough. *Hōkūleʻa* began to list, and then the starboard hull went under. Within minutes *Hōkūleʻa* had capsized, floating upside down with both masts broken and the sails in shreds. The crew members were either in the water and holding on to the boat or straddling the ridged bottom of one of the two hulls. Wet, cold, and a few of them severely bruised, they would all hold on for the next twenty-two hours.

Eddie Aikau had only one thought: Rescue. *Hōkūleʻa* was only 12 miles southwest of Lānaʻi, and Eddie was sure he could make it on his surfboard. After all, he had ridden Waimea Bay at 25 feet plus. He had also rescued more than a thousand people in high surf on the North Shore during the previous nine years as head lifeguard at Waimea Bay. As the night wore on, Eddie pleaded with Dave Lyman to let him go for shore and help. Eddie figured it was their only chance. When dawn broke, Lyman could see they were drifting south. If they were not spotted by an aircraft soon, they would drift beyond the interisland flight paths. Eddie persisted. The one radio on board was in the starboard hull, which had been flooded. It was a panicky situation. Sixteen people, no food, no water, 30- to 40-knot winds and 12- to 18-foot seas. Hope was fading fast.

At 10:00 A.M. Friday morning, Lyman gave in to Eddie's prodding. It seemed to be their only chance. Armed with flares, wearing a yellow life jacket, and tied to his cream-white surfboard, Eddie said good-bye to his friends and headed for Lānaʻi. It was the last time anyone ever saw Eddie Aikau.

Eddie's Legacy

What was it in the core of his being that sent Eddie on his rescue mission? I asked his brother Clyde this question many years later. Clyde described having missed his brother for a long, long time. He had been terribly lonely without him. Clyde and Eddie had done everything together— surfing, work, partying, diving—they were very close. Clyde believes Eddie's decision after *Hōkūleʻa* capsized was automatic. Eddie's life was all about saving lives. In 1971, Eddie had been named Lifeguard of the Year by the City and County of Honolulu. Though he rescued more than a thousand people, he seldom filled out a rescue report. His supervisor, Captain Chillingsworth, could not get Eddie to write things down. Eddie was too busy thinking about people out there in the water who might need help. Seeing his friends on *Hōkūleʻa* that night, cold and full of fear, would have played on his strongest instincts to help people in trouble. Clyde described it as Eddie all the way. He had to go.

After Eddie set off on his surfboard, *Hōkūleʻa* drifted for about ten hours. Miraculously, the current changed direction, heading west instead of south. The crew managed to retrieve several flares that had been sealed

March 18, 1978, Hōkūleʻa under a 15-hour tow by the Coast Guard back to Honolulu after capsizing in Molokaʻi Channel. Photo courtesy of the Honolulu Advertiser.

*Eddie Aikau in the early
1970s, atop a Waimea giant.
Leroy Grannis photo.*

in watertight containers, and when night fell into darkness, they set
one after another ablaze. At 8:32 P.M. a Hawaiian Airlines pilot spotted
Hōkūleʻa and radioed the Coast Guard. In just two hours, several heli-
copters were on the scene, airlifting twelve of the remaining fifteen crew
members to safety. Dave Lyman and two others stayed with *Hōkūleʻa*
until a Coast Guard cutter arrived early Saturday morning.

That same day, we left the pier at Makapuʻu on the *Holokai* at about
7:00 A.M. By late morning we were approaching the area where we guessed
the *Hōkūleʻa* had foundered. The seas were 12 to 18 feet, and some were
cresting—breaking—in the open ocean. For Eddie still to be alive, he
would have had to survive in a wild ocean for more than twenty-four
hours. It was unlikely for anyone, except perhaps Eddie. Bob Lundy, a
close friend of Eddie's and a North Shore big-wave surfer, gave Eddie a
fifty-fifty chance. We were trying our best to improve the odds. Late in the
afternoon, *Holokai* was taking 50-degree rolls, and the skipper informed
me that we would have to give up the search. The wind was blowing about
45 knots, so strong it was tearing the tops off the waves. You could hardly
tell where the sky stopped and the ocean began. Seeing Eddie, had he
been there, would have been nearly impossible.

For the next four days, the Coast Guard conducted a search of all the channels out to about 100 miles. The Aikau family rented a helicopter and conducted their own search. On Saturday the 18th, the day after Eddie left *Hōkūleʻa*, his brother spotted a surfboard from the air 28 miles south of Koko Head on Oʻahu but it was never retrieved. The board looked as if it had a red stripe running across the nose, raising doubt about whether it was Eddie's. The Aikau family continued their search for four more days. They combed every shoreline on four islands—Lānaʻi, Molokaʻi, Oʻahu, and Kauaʻi. Even today, Clyde prefers to say that Eddie was "lost at sea." Not drowned. Clyde dreams that Eddie may have made it. That he may be on some island in the Pacific, his memory gone, but still alive, still Eddie.

Clyde knows that Eddie's place in history is set. Winner of the Duke Kahanamoku contest, considered the best big-wave rider in his time at Waimea Bay, a lifeguard with no one even close to his record of saving lives. Clyde describes Eddie's life as having been full. At thirty-two, he was young, had a beautiful wife, a terrific job, played slack-key guitar, and had a red Volkswagen bus filled with surfboards—he was happy. Eddie had been on the verge of death many times before at Waimea Bay in huge surf. His heart and his soul had pulled him through. He didn't do it for fame; it was love. It was Eddie's romance with the ocean.

When Clyde goes surfing these days, he follows the turtles. During the first big-wave contest at Waimea Bay to honor the memory of his brother —the Eddie Aikau contest—Clyde Aikau was entered. It was 1986, almost ten years after the *Hōkūleʻa* accident. The surf was 20 to 25 feet and ultra-gnarly, west, ledging, almost unrideable. During Clyde's heat, he saw two turtles, swimming at the surface and began to follow them. They led him to the precise lineup where he would catch wave after wave that day. It was perfect. Clyde kept returning to the spot the turtles had shown him. A ghostly feeling came over him. He sensed the spirits of his brother and Jose Angel (another big-wave surfer, who drowned diving for black coral) in the two turtles. Clyde felt totally at one with the sea. Natural. Nothing could go wrong. He rode wave after wave, never thinking about his score or his place in the competition. When the final horn sounded, Clyde Aikau had won the Eddie.

Years before Clyde won the 1986 contest, farewell ceremonies for Eddie and Jose Angel had been held at Waimea Bay to honor them after they died. I attended both ceremonies. Everyone paddled their boards to the lineup, formed a large circle, and held hands while symbolic ashes (their bodies were never found) were spread in the water on the lineup. More than four hundred surfers removed the lei they were wearing and left them in the middle of the circle. In 1996, Mark Foo's ashes were spread in Waimea Bay in the same place, in the same way. And perhaps one day Clyde's and mine will be, too. It is a tradition the turtles have come to know.

The surfing community bid aloha to Eddie Aikau in a ceremony at Waimea Bay, where Eddie worked and saved more than one thousand lives, and rode countless 20-foot waves. Sylvain Cazenave photo.

145

17 THE MODERN SURF GLADIATORS AND THE OUTER REEFS

To experience the ultimate thrill
You must be willing to pay the ultimate price.

Mark Sheldon Foo

Point Surf, Mākaha (leeward coast, Oʻahu) and Waimea Bay (North Shore, Oʻahu), Todos Santos (Baja California), Maverick's (northern California), and now the outer reefs in Hawaiʻi, most prominently Jaws (Maui), mark the significant surf spots in the evolving history of big-wave riding. They also represent a progression in both size and danger of the waves that break at each spot. In chapters 3 and 4, I trace the history of big-wave riding, beginning with Mākaha in the 1950s and then on the North Shore with my own personal experiences in the '60s. Since then, both places have been a Mecca for anyone who would take up the challenge of being a big-wave rider. I've been in the lineup now for some forty-odd years, and I've watched two or three generations of big-wave riders mature, reach their peak, and then gradually give way to the next cohort of up-and-coming matadors. The number of the truly committed in any one generation has never exceeded a dozen or so. However, there's a growing fringe group of guys who go out but rarely ride. The truly committed are the men who ride as long as it's rideable, no matter how big it gets. Waimea Bay in the 1990s on a medium-good day at 15 to 18 feet attracts more than one hundred surfers; fifty or sixty might be out on the lineup at any one time. It's a zoo. Five or six riders may be on every wave. At 20 feet, the number drops by half, but it is still overcrowded. Even then, more than a dozen are floundering around, invariably in the wrong spot or in the way. At 25 to 30 feet, the number shrinks to the totally committed, only four or five riders. Their names are predictable: Ken Bradshaw, Darrick Doerner, Brock Little, James Jones, Clyde Aikau, and, until recently, Mark Foo. They're the modern gladiators of big-wave riding today.

Another "wave" of master athletes is the group that surfs Jaws, on Maui; the gladiators there are Laird Hamilton, Dave Kalama, Pete

Darrick Doerner charging Jaws for his first time. Sylvain Cazenave photo.

Cabrinha, Rush Randle, Mark Angulo, Josh Stone, and Robby Naish. They have recently been joined by a handful of big-wave riders from O'ahu, including Darrick Doerner, Brock Little, Buzzy Kerbox, and Brian Keaulana. But before the story of Jaws, let's return to the North Shore of O'ahu for a look at the men who are currently at the top of a sport about to enter its sixth decade.

Ken Bradshaw (center) and Brock Little (inside) take the drop at Waimea Bay. Sylvain Cazenave photo.

Ken Bradshaw

Ken Bradshaw grew up in Texas. After chewing up the football field and many adversaries during his high school years, Kenny (to his friends) discovered surfing at a funky little place on the Gulf Coast called Surfside. Despite mushy peaks, the call of the surf captured Ken's imagination. He seemed to be destined to tackle the biggest and baddest waves on the planet. Ken's dreams were filled with Hawai'i. After several years surfing California waves, Ken arrived on the North Shore of O'ahu in the winter of 1971–72. In those early years, he charged Sunset and Waimea with the same fanatical vigor that characterized the big-wave pioneers in the '50s and '60s. True grit and thunder-and-lightning were his trademarks. Kenny undeniably had the energy and the heart to surf big waves.

Over the years, Kenny Bradshaw has become addicted to Waimea Bay. When it is breaking and he can't be there, he is tormented. It eats at him; his rightful place is there, in the lineup. At Waimea, he is in his element. Kenny won the Duke Kahanamoku in 1982, one of the last years it was held. The Duke was a competition created for the original big-wave riders to prove themselves on an Olympic playing field. By winning one of the last Dukes, Kenny connected himself to the ranks of first-generation big-wave riders. From there, his contribution has been catalytic. First, he led the present-day generation of big-wave riders to push the limits of mastering Waimea at 25 to 30 feet plus. Then, he launched the modern assault on the outer reefs of the North Shore. There, Bradshaw and company are pioneering a new era in the history of surfing.

The outer reefs to Kenny represent a new frontier in big-wave surfing. The major breakthrough that opened the door was the development of jet skis, used for towing surfers into massive swells before the waves break on the outer reefs. Out there, giant waves are almost impossible to line up. And they are moving so fast, it is extremely difficult to catch them. Paddling speed is a limiting factor. Jet skis put a surfer on the face before it becomes vertical. This solves the problem of catching the wave, but then, of course, comes the problem of riding it!

Ken Bradshaw with his jet ski and stringer of boards. Sylvain Cazenave photo.

Kenny Bradshaw believes every surfer who wants to surf the outer reefs should first do it under their own power. He says, "If you have to rely on a jet ski, you shouldn't be out there." It can look deceptively easy. Kenny warns, "People can get access who are not prepared mentally or physically. People will die."

It's a tough way to look at it but Kenny is probably right. "A surfer," he says, "should know his physical limits for swimming, breath holding, and body strength to take the horrendous hits and pummeling that come with riding waves this large [30 feet plus]. One should also have the ability to ride Waimea at its maximum limits." Were these rules of entry to the outer reefs followed, very few surfers would qualify.

Bradshaw's greatest wish is to surf uncrowded waves. That's what pushed him to explore the outer reefs in the first place. His second dream concerns equipment. As a premier shaper of big-wave guns, Kenny gets "chicken skin" thinking about all the design possibilities that apply to tow-in surfing. Surfboards used for tow-in surfing today are already different from the typical big-wave guns of 10 feet or longer from a few years ago. Tow-in boards are short, heavy, and narrow. You don't need paddling speed to catch the wave, and once you are in it, greater weight adds stability and glide. Overall, it rides smoother. A narrow board is freed up for rail-to-rail high-speed turning. Tow-in surfers are only beginning to test the possibilities, and the learning curve is mind-boggling. Instead of catching one or two big waves an hour, with a jet ski you can ride ten waves an hour. Kenny calls it Richter, "off the chart." He says, "The future is limited only by our imagination." From those mushy little peaks off Surfside in Texas in the 1960s, Kenny Bradshaw has joined the elite inner circle of the best in the world in big waves. Not bad for a Texas greenhorn.

Darrick Doerner

Darrick Doerner was born in Fresno, California. He doesn't have much to say about his life before he arrived in Hawai'i at age sixteen. Before that Darrick was bouncing around from school to school, town to town, state to state, a vagabond kid of vagabond parents. Surfing was his escape. Hawai'i was a lifeline to freedom. Darrick joined the big-wave scene slowly, with ups and downs. He didn't do it "straight," like Bradshaw. For a time drugs plagued Darrick, but he succeeded in shaking them off. Gradually, lifeguarding and big waves straightened him out.

In the 1980s, Darrick Doerner dominated at Waimea Bay. On Super Bowl Sunday in 1988, he rode a solid 30-footer. He became airborne on the wave, but his windsurfing experience pulled him through. He made the drop, and he made the wave. Randy Rarick rates him number one for sheer guts: "When everyone else is heading in, Darrick is still charging. He doesn't have a limit this side of death."

In 1990, I described Darrick Doerner's attributes as a big-wave rider in Bruce Jenkins' excellent book *North Shore Chronicles.* I described Darrick as "wiry, built like a cheetah, light, but extremely strong. His muscles are like steel wires. He is perfectly suited to big-wave riding. You don't want to be too big. You need paddling speed, explosive strength, high agility and, of course, you must be fearless, maybe even crazy."

Robby Naish, too, credits Darrick Doerner for pushing the Jaws crew on Maui up a notch or two. Before Darrick arrived on the scene, many of the guys at Jaws were shoulder soldiers, content merely to coast down the face and make the wave. At 25 or 30 feet, it seemed like a perfectly acceptable tactic. Then Darrick pushed the envelope further by deeper and deeper tow-ins, pulling into insane barrels and still making the waves. Doerner has upped the ante everywhere he has surfed—Waimea, Jaws,

and the outer reefs. Bradshaw describes Doerner as extremely talented, naturally gifted. Darrick's latest game is kite surfing, riding deep ocean swells behind a large sailcloth powered by the wind. This is a game that opens up the whole ocean to surfing. Where it takes Darrick and the other surfers who will follow is unknown. But for a man who has already tested the bounds of the biggest waves anywhere in the world, it might be safe to say that he has no limit.

Mark Foo

Mark Foo was high strung. Taut. Mark talked so fast it was difficult to understand him. Even as master of ceremonies on his TV show, he had a machine-gun delivery. Eyes darting, voice stopping and starting, never finishing a sentence—in fact, usually nonstop talking, pausing only to breathe. Mark Foo was a stoked guy. Oddly, he described himself as the opposite of a type-A personality. He would say that he was extremely conservative, calculating, afraid of speed, afraid of heights, not inclined to gamble or take risks. He claimed that when he was ten years old, he had been afraid of the water.

Mark Sheldon Foo was born in Singapore of Chinese parents. He didn't learn to surf or even swim until his parents moved to Hawai'i when he was ten. His introduction to the sport was in Waikīkī at Baby Queen's and Canoes, then Kaiser's and Ala Moana. From there he tried the North Shore, first at Chun's, then Hale'iwa, then Velzeyland. His entree into the sport was gradual, calculated. By the time Mark was ready to challenge Sunset, he was totally committed. In his adolescent years, surfing had become his passion, an obsession. Mark felt that surfing was the only pure form of happiness. It was one of life's secrets, something most people never discover. On one hand Mark was a loner, self-absorbed and even selfish in his hunger to catch every wave; on the other hand, he wanted to share surfing with the world. That was the other side of his personality—the promoter, the entrepreneur. Surfing seemed to be the perfect outlet for him. Riding big surf requires intensity and high energy. It also requires an inner strength, an ability to control emotions. All this showed in Mark's imperturbable face. Surfing was also a means to gain recognition, even fame, for those who rose to the top of the sport.

By the time he was seventeen, Mark was a true surf addict. He had first reached for the golden ring in one contest after the other, but after half a dozen years of not making it, Mark refocused his energy on a bigger prize—riding the biggest wave in history. Mark's greatest skills were not those required for small waves. He lacked the acrobatic finesse of the younger and more agile high-performance athletes on the professional circuit. Mark's forte was more mental or physical-mental. His strength

was the meeting place of mind and body, desire and power, Zen, and physical training. During the 1980s and '90s, Mark Foo did rise to the top of big-wave riding, when he and about four or five others reigned as the kings of Waimea.

Mark used to say, "You have to be willing to pay the ultimate price to experience the ultimate thrill." Mark dreamed of discovering and riding waves even bigger than at Waimea Bay. He was one of the first to venture beyond the normal breaks at Waimea and Sunset to the outer reefs. Deep in the back of his mind, Mark's ultimate plan was to discover Destination-X, the place in his imagination where the greatest waves roamed on earth. It was this quest, in fact, that led Mark to his last ride.

The place was Maverick's, a cold, desolate outpost on the northern California coast. The date was December 23, 1994. The night before, Mark Foo, Ken Bradshaw, and Brock Little flew from Hawai'i to surf Maverick's —to be part of history. What happened was indeed history.

Mark's last wave was not his biggest. His biggest wave had been ten years earlier at Waimea Bay on January 18, 1985. People who saw it said it was a freak of freak waves. Maybe 35 feet high. Though Mark didn't make it to the bottom before being tossed into the air and pulverized by tons of avalanching water, surely his destiny to ride the biggest wave was fulfilled that day at Waimea. The ride was at least equal to the biggest wave ever ridden up to that time. That ten years later he was still searching for yet a bigger wave reflects how driven Mark Foo really was.

Maverick's swallowed him up on another freak wave, a monster not for size, at 15 to 18 feet, but for being ugly and absolutely unruly. Ken Bradshaw pulled off it, wanting no part of the drop. Mark stayed with it,

Mark Foo's last wave. In the second photo of the sequence, notice the tip of Mark's board catching a chop. This instantaneous break in speed pitched Mark forward off his board and led to his disastrous wipeout. Laurence Beck photos.

but the bottom sucked out, and pitched Mark out into space. No one knows exactly what happened next. When they found his body an hour later, it was floating face down. A small indentation on his forehead suggested that he hit either the bottom or his board. During the wipeout his board broke into three pieces, leading some to speculate that he did hit his board and was knocked unconscious underwater.

Mark died as he had lived, in pursuit of a dream. His ashes were laid to rest three weeks later at Waimea Bay, joining those of Eddie Aikau and Jose Angel. Mark Foo reached Destination-X, and his soul is now resting there in peace.

James Jones

Since 1970, when James Jones first surfed Waimea Bay, he has been a constant member of the lineup there. He has hit virtually every swell to break at Waimea in twenty-six seasons. Not only that, but no other big-wave rider comes close to his batting average. James Jones makes 90 percent of the waves he takes off on. As great as his contemporaries may be, most of them are lucky to hit 75 percent on a big day at the Bay. And for size, James has ridden Waimea as big as it gets.

James grew up on the south shore of Oʻahu, learning to surf much like Mark Foo at various spots in Waikīkī. Born in 1952, James was barely a teenager when the North Shore surf was first pioneered. Fred Van Dyke, one of the earliest to challenge the giant waves, was James' seventh-grade

James Jones, master shaper and surfer, with one of his big-wave guns. Sylvain Cazenave photo.

teacher at Punahou School in Honolulu. James was awestruck with admiration and respect for Fred. Van Dyke taught him that big-wave riding is a science. The training, equipment, breath holding, understanding of currents, knowing where to paddle out, how to get in, wave judgment, analyzing weather charts, on and on—the subject was bigger than any topic covered in class. Big-wave surfing was to become James' life.

Today, James Jones is distinguished for his intelligence in the water. On every set, he is in precisely the right spot. If he doesn't take a wave, it may be out of courtesy to another surfer, or it could be because the wave is a rogue—he senses something inherently wrong with it. James' judgment is impeccable. Van Dyke's schooling paid off. James' idea is to make the wave. He doesn't count wipeouts as waves caught. By that standard, many of the world's biggest waves "ridden" would be considered only attempts. James applies this pure philosophy to tow-in surfing on the outer reefs. He does not consider it real surfing. According to James Jones, it's the jet ski, not the surfer, that catches the wave. To James, riding that big-wave is the ultimate personal experience—just you and the wave, perfect harmony, a love affair. He says, "To be honest, you've got to catch the wave yourself."

What about the outer reefs and the future according to James Jones? For himself, he is not interested in the outer reefs. His ideal is mastery of the skill necessary to do it yourself, alone. James believes you have to rule Waimea first. Too many guys are leaping at the chance to do the outer reefs without sufficient training. Ken Bradshaw agrees, even to the extent of floating an idea to offer a course in tow-in surfing. It would include basic training, CPR, rescue skills, and radio communication, plus evaluating whether someone has the requisite guts and skills to ride Waimea.

James Jones does not plan to enroll. He is already a full professor of riding the biggest surf that Waimea has to deliver. It has earned him a place in surfing history as a master big-wave surgeon. At 140 pounds and forty-six years old, James Jones doesn't have to prove anything to anyone. And though he's been there and done that, James Jones is still very much on the scene, hitting 90 percent. Olé.

Other Modern Masters of Big-Wave Riding

Clyde Aikau, Brock Little, Brian Keaulana, and Keone Downing round out the group of surfers I regard as the best of the present generation. They all surf the heavies at a skill level on a par with the other big four described above. The only difference perhaps is the regularity with which they are found in the lineup. Each, of course, has his own style.

Clyde Aikau is Eddie Aikau's brother. Over the years, when either one was in the lineup, they dominated. Eddie lost his life trying to save his shipmates on the *Hōkūleʻa,* but before that he was the unspoken master of Waimea. His reign was short but not often challenged during the mid 1970s. Clyde too was always extremely powerful in big waves. His style was strong and quiet— strong, quiet, and, I might add, handsome. Clyde won the Eddie Aikau memorial competition 1986 with a show of truly inspired big-wave surfing in 25-foot waves at Waimea Bay.

Keone Downing and Brian Keaulana are virtuoso examples of masters in big surf. Like his father, George Downing, Keone is cunning, calm, collected, and incredibly coordinated—undeniably a great surfer. Keone won the second Eddie Aikau contest at Waimea in 20- to 25-foot surf in January 1990.

Brock Little was also in the 1990 contest. His rides were the most spectacular of the day. One in particular probably was the largest successful tube ride ever at Waimea. Brock might have won that day but for several wipeouts. His bravado sometimes exceeded his judgment.

Brian Keaulana is another son of a great pioneer in the sport of kings. His father, Buffalo, will forever be known as the king of Mākaha. Buffalo did everything in the water—he rode big waves, bodysurfed like a seal, speared fish for his family, paddled canoe, surfed canoe, won tandem contests, stood on his head, and on top of all this, he is one of the nicest people I've ever met. His son Brian is an aliʻi, too. He stands erect. He is well muscled. His face bears the look of a Hawaiian king. At Point Surf, Mākaha, at 20 feet plus, Brian Keaulana is now the king. No one touches

Brian Keaulana and his wife, Nobleen—local power and local beauty

him. The Waimea bunch, the Jaws gang, the new breed of tow-in dare-devils, none come close to the son of Buffalo at Mākaha. It is Brian's turf. Brian Keaulana will be the Duke Kahanamoku of the twenty-first century.

Others coming up through the ranks are bursting with energy to ride better and bigger waves, but like the coming of the next century, which will bring new storms to rage across the Pacific and generate massive swells on Hawai'i's North Shore, their stories will have to wait.

Laird performing at Jaws, in the teeth of the monster, with his specially designed surfboard with footstraps. Sylvain Cazenave photos.

The Outer Reefs

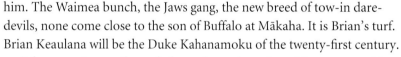

The complete story of surfing the outer reefs probably will not be told until the next century. Actually, the story began about twenty-five years ago. Once upon a time, back then, there was a wildman by the name of Jim Neece. In 1972, Wildman Neece claimed he would ride 50-foot waves at Ka'ena Point. It was a fairly safe boast because waves that big come along only about once every twenty-five years or so. I've seen it this size and rideable once in my life. Two years after his claim, Neece disappeared from the big-wave surfing scene in Hawai'i. Before long a new Evel Knievel surfaced. This time it was Charlie Galento, and again the story was more talk than show. About 1975, Jose Angel, Jeff Johnson, and Flippy Hoffman caught the tow-in bug. They recruited me to drive their 14-foot Boston Whaler. We practiced a time or two at Sunset and once at

Jaws with jet ski and surfer, a moment after the surfer dropped the tow-in line. Sylvain Cazenave photo.

Ka'ena Point in 15-foot surf. To survive the horrendous wipeouts, Jose had rigged a small SCUBA bottle with 300 pounds of air pressure strapped to his back in nylon webbing. All systems worked fine, but before the really big waves showed up, Jose met a tragic and untimely death diving for black coral off Maui.

A lull slowed the assault on Ka'ena and the outer reefs during the late 1970s and '80s. Big-wave riding took a back seat to small-wave hotdogging, professional contests, and high performance. The media co-opted the sport, and the buzz was dominated by the *Who's Who* personalities on the world contest tour, sponsors, commercial hype, magazine ads, and money. The outer reefs would remain dormant for another ten years.

During this time, several new developments gradually began to focus attention in the surfing world back toward big waves and the outer reefs. Windsurfing exploded on the scene and Hawai'i's Robby Naish was world champion for ten years running. In the meantime, Robby, being a good board surfer, was already windsurfing waves at Ho'okipa on Maui and Backyard's on O'ahu in the 1980s. Gradually, other windsurfers began riding bigger and bigger waves and moving out into deeper and deeper water to do it. Then Jaws was discovered.

Jaws used to be called Atom Blasters. It was first windsurfed by the Angulo brothers in the late 1980s. To the locals watching from the beach, their windsurfer sails looked so small that they renamed the place Jaws.

Like Waimea Bay, Maverick's, and Todos Santos, the swell at Jaws focuses on an underwater, V-shaped reef running offshore and moves in where it meets a shallow shelf. The top of the shelf is about 25 feet deep, the same depth as Waimea and Maverick's. As the swell moves in across the ridge it almost doubles in size. Because of abrupt shoaling, the wave ends up breaking in the form of a top-to-bottom tube.

Before long, surfers followed the windsurfers to Jaws, but they were terrified by the sudden, steep drop. Frequent strong winds also made it difficult to surf much over 15 feet. It became immediately obvious that the wave had to be caught at a point earlier than you could accomplish by paddling alone. Watching the windsurfers coast into wave faces from outside gave immediate rebirth to the whole idea of tow-in surfing. This time it would not be a passing fad. The idea took hold and established a new frontier of surfing.

Why tow-in surfing suddenly exploded in popularity in the early 1990s can probably be traced to two trends: increased crowds in the water and technological developments. Crowds have indeed become a menacing factor, particularly at Waimea Bay. The outer reefs represent a haven, an escape, and an even bigger challenge to those who have reached the limits in conventional big-wave riding.

Enter jet skis in about 1990, faster and more maneuverable than Boston Whalers or Zodiacs, and the new sport of tow-in surfing takes off. The equipment—board design—has also advanced markedly. Today, the typical tow-in board is 7'6", 18" wide, and 24 pounds. The tail is stubby, with

Robby Naish on a spectacular wave at Backyards, Sunset Beach, Hawai'i. Another windsurfer, Curt Carlsmith, was killed minutes after this shot was taken. Sylvain Cazenave photo.

side-set twin fins all the way back. The nose is upturned and narrow to buffer the wind and chop on the face. Footstraps, taken from windsurfing, are used to hold the feet in place. On some boards, lead weights are implanted below the footstraps for added stability. Another technological advance has been weather information: buoys, satellite data, weather fax machines, and wave forecasting. These days, when the tow-in teams attack the outer reefs, they know exactly what to expect for wave size, tide and current conditions, and the wind. They have it down to a science, to the point where they can accurately predict the very hour the surf will peak.

So, who are the best of this new breed of outer-reef men? It's difficult to say. There are many up-and-coming risk-takers who have the talent to pull it off—too many to list here. At Jaws, Robby Naish is most impressed with Dave Kalama, for his fluid style and aggressive spirit, and Peter Cabrinha for his overall ability, especially backside. Robby describes Laird Hamilton as the most confident, the most powerful—as a man who must have balls of steel. Then, of course, there are Darrick Doerner and Robby himself. Robby Naish has got to be one of the all-time greatest athletes in any sport, dominating world-class windsurfing for more than two decades.

Where do the limits end in big-wave surfing? Have they been reached at Waimea Bay, Maverick's, and now the outer reefs? Are there other big-wave spots yet to be discovered? If so, where? The ski company K-2 has challenged the big-wave riders of the world to catch (by paddling alone) the biggest wave in the North Pacific Ocean. The prize is $50,000. The winner for the first year ('97–'98) of this amazing contest was announced on March 31, 1998. Taylor Knox, a twenty-seven-year-old professional surfer from Carlsbad, California, won the prize. His conquest was a 52-foot monster ridden February 16, 1998, at Todos Santos. Mike Parsons, who witnessed the ride, said that Knox was airborn on the take-off. He gave Knox a 10 percent chance of making the drop, later calling the successful ride a feat of remarkable skill and athleticism.

And what about the future? Will the K-2 pursuit end with the death of one or more surfers? And what about other ways to conquer big waves in the ocean? Will tow-ins be recognized as totally legitimate? Will a surfer one day ride a rogue wave or a giant tsunami? Where the limits lie in big waves is difficult to predict. My sense is that they will be pushed far beyond anything that we can now imagine.

Tomorrow's generation of big-wave riders will discover the answers to these questions. The big-wave riders of the past and the present will pass the baton to them. And while they inherit fifty or more years of surfing wisdom and experience, their goals will be even more difficult to reach than ours were. And as we pass the baton, I say to them as Duke Kahanamoku once said to me, "Take our spirit and continue to surf those big blue birds."

18 LIFE AND DEATH IN THE OCEAN

Because I could not stop for Death,
He kindly stopped for me;
The carriage held but just ourselves
and immortality.

Emily Dickenson

Golden lads and girls all must,
as chimney-sweepers, come to dust.

Shakespeare
CYMBELINE

The ocean is the primordial birthplace for life on earth. It is the source of the amniotic fluid of all cellular life. The ocean is also the ultimate final resting place for all things on earth. If all of the land masses of all the continents and islands were to erode into the sea, its average depth would still be about 8,000 feet. Then, only ocean and atmosphere would cover the earth. Waves would circle the planet unimpeded by the land. Life, then as now, would be a continuous cycle of birth and death, of constant renewal. Each of us, acting out our life, is a member of this cycle. Many of us sense ourselves to be like molecules or atoms, part of a larger whole, an unending cycle. Ocean waves are another cycle of life and death. Sublimely, they remind us of our mortality.

Like Eugenie Clark, Rell Sunn was Hawai'i's lady with a spear. Her surfboard served as a diving kit for fins, mask, and spear. Dennis Oda photo.

Nick Gabalon

My first encounter with death in the ocean was when I was fourteen years old. It was 1951 at Malibu Beach, California. A bunch of the boys had been out surfing all day. It was a super day; the surf was 6 to 8 feet and the guys were riding all the way to the pier before pulling out. Late that afternoon, Nick Gabalon caught a beauty of a wave all by himself. I watched him sliding, irrevocably committed, sliding and sliding on that 8-foot wall. Nick was a huge man, heavily muscled and a terrific athlete. He was the only black surfer on the entire California coast. On that wave, he seemed to go and go, like he was in a trance. As he neared the pier he kept sliding and sliding, like it wasn't even there. He disappeared right into one of the

pilings. Three days later his body was spotted floating offshore. I remember paddling out, not knowing exactly why—probably to be sure it was Nick. After paddling 400 or 500 yards out, I could see his body floating face-down. A seagull sat perched on his bloated back, which had turned white after three days' immersion in the ocean. The bird was pecking at his flesh. I remember thinking then how fleeting life is, how it can be snatched away in an instant. How insignificant we all are. Death contradicts human importance. It shatters ego. The sight was devastating to me, but somehow it helped me grow stronger.

Nick had been our postman when I was growing up. We became friends when I learned he was a surfer. He was about ten years older than me, and I looked up to him as I did Buzzy Trent. Nick wrote the poem "Lost Lives" six days before he lost his life.

Nick's death had a profound effect on my life. It made me realize that the "here and now" is all we have. We can mourn the death of those we have loved and lost, and that may give us strength, but death is final. There is no way to undo it. It is so starkly absolute that I realized even then why humankind invented an afterlife: There had to be a way to soften the blow. Nick's death taught me to celebrate life—his and, of course, my own. It was one more lesson learned from the ocean.

Over the Edge

Over the years while I have been surfing, diving, and studying the ocean, several of my friends and colleagues have been claimed by the sea. Like Nick Gabalon's death, their loss has been a lesson I have learned over and over again, but it never gets any easier. The possibility of death comes with the risk of being on the water, in the ocean. It is something the big-wave riders talk about and accept. For example, Jose Angel and

I often talked about how close we were to the edge of death while surfing giant waves at Waimea Bay. We would train during the summers by skin diving 60 feet deep for green turtles off the North Shore reefs. We calculated that during wipeouts at Waimea we could stay down for two waves if we had to, about thirty seconds. With our hearts beating about one hundred times a minute, this is about maximum. We also ran in soft sand and then held our breath. After running about 100 yards, again thirty seconds was about all we could muster, but most of us could hold our breath for more than three minutes in a resting position on land. One day at Waimea I discovered in the middle of a wipeout that there was so much air in the whitewater that I could actually breath underwater by sucking foam through my fingers. It worked but it wasn't something I relied on very often.

Jose Angel had no fear of death. He was full-on, as though the purpose of life was to live "within no limits." Only then could he be fulfilled. Jose went over the edge that separates life and death at least two dozen times but always managed to claw his way back. Back for another smile, another wave, another throw of the dice. Greg Noll did the same thing. I think we all looked over that edge into the abyss, into the darkness from which there could be no return, many times. It was like blinking death in the face.

To do this was both humbling and empowering. Every time I came close to drowning (perhaps ten times), I felt both emotions: unimportance and exuberance for life. On one hand, I felt as important as a grain of sand destined to one day join other grains of sand on the bottom. But at the same time, I felt I had also managed to cheat death. That emotion supercharged me for life, though not without a measure of caution. The supercharge was addicting, but I understood it was a seduction that could kill me. At some point I would have to say, enough.

The Unrelenting Sea

My day of reckoning came gradually, through a series of tragedies. In 1976, I lost my friend Jose Angel to diving for black coral. In 1978, Eddie Aikau was lost at sea. In that same year, we lost two divers launching the *Star II* submarine in the quest to harvest pink coral off Makapu'u. Later that same year, ten University of Hawai'i oceanographers were swallowed up by the sea on board the *Holoholo.* The ship disappeared during the peak of a perfect storm in the middle of the Alenuihaha Channel between Maui and Hawai'i in 35- to 40-foot seas. Besides these friends and colleagues, one or two surfers disappear in big surf on the North Shore every year. One of the most tragic losses in the surfing community was Mark Foo.

Leaving the bottom at 225 feet off Lahaina, Maui, Jose Angel waves on his way to the surface with a large black coral tree. I took this photograph the day before he died. It seemed as though he was waving good-bye.

163

Two thousand well-wishers paid their respects to Mark Foo two weeks after his death in December 1994. His ashes were spread on the waters of Waimea Bay, where they joined those of Eddie Aikau. Sylvain Cazenave photo.

The day before Mark's death, I had surfed with him at Sunset Beach. Late in the afternoon, after surfing, we had a beer together at my house at Sunset Beach. His girlfriend, Lisa Nakano, and my wife, Maria, were trying to talk Mark out of going to California the next day to surf Maverick's. It was two days before Christmas. Sunset Beach was as perfect as it gets, 10 to 12 feet with light offshore winds, and clean. Why go to California? Mark explained that Maverick's had been going off all week at 25 to 30 feet. He felt he couldn't miss it, that it was part of his destiny to be there. Mark had promised Ken Bradshaw and Brock Little he'd go, as all three had been hired to do a photo shoot at Maverick's. The die was cast.

Losing Mark brought all of us to our knees. It brought together the whole community of big-wave riders in Hawai'i. It reinforced our brotherhood, our love and respect for each other, and for life itself. We still ride the big ones but ever so much more carefully. The ocean gives rich pleasure but it also takes it away. Like the white whale in *Moby Dick,* the sea has no mercy. It recognizes no ego, no differences among people, no self-imposed importance. The sea is unrelenting. It is all-powerful. Perhaps by testing ourselves against such power, we test our mortality. Will death's carriage stop for us? When it doesn't, you feel an exaggerated sense of immortality. This feeling, together with the sheer thrill and fun of it, raises life to an ultimate high. Woody Brown said it well: "When you make a big one, your heart is on fire and your soul is filled with pride." Such crowning moments define our lives.

Rell Sunn, Child of the Sea

Rell Sunn was the Duke Kahanamoku of women's surfing in Hawai'i. Like me, Rell was superinterested in oceanography and spearfishing, and we often talked about coral reef ecology and the need to conserve reef fish populations in Hawai'i. In 1993, she and I were invited to Biarritz, France, together with a team of other Hawaiian surfers. On this trip I first realized how sick Rell had been, though she never complained about her illness. Being with Rell in Europe, I also became more aware of her charm and her role as a global ambassador for the sport of surfing. No one carried the spirit of aloha with more dignity and grace.

Rell's daughter, Jan; brother, Eric; husband, Dave Parmenter; and Brian Keaulana surf with Rell's ashes on her last wave.

Rell died January 2, 1998, at the age of forty-seven, after a fourteen-year battle with breast cancer. The sea was her sustaining force. The sea did not take Rell's life, it gave Rell a passion not to give up. It gave her spirit, energy, and the will to live. She kept surfing almost to the very end. Her husband, Dave Parmenter, took her to Mākaha before she died, so that she could be lowered into the water and taste saltwater on her lips. Two weeks after her death, on January 17, 1998, about three thousand friends and family gathered at Mākaha to say good-bye. It was a Rell kind of day, misty with salt spray in the air and surf 4 to 6 feet. After the eulogy and music, fifty painted doves were released into the air. Their flight created a rainbow of color over the crowd on the beach. In a canoe, with her daughter, Jan, her brother, Eric, and her husband, Dave, and Brian Keaulana steering, Rell was taken out to sea to catch her last wave. Sitting in the front of the canoe, Dave Parmenter held the urn containing Rell's ashes high overhead as the canoe surfed from the outside blowhole all the way to the beach. I was standing on the shore watching the ceremony with Fred Hemmings and Randy Rarick and their wives. When we saw Rell on that last wave, we were emotionally overwhelmed—a shiver of awe, love, and respect for her ran through me. It was Rell's wave to immortality.

19 TWO REALITIES: A PHILOSOPHY OF LIFE

There are only atoms and opinions.

Albert Einstein

Reality is in the mind of the beholder. How then can you separate the real from the unreal, and why is it important to talk about here? First, it determines the way people live their lives. It determined the way I have lived mine. In the broadest sense, it is the subject of this book. It's important, too, because it addresses the "What is real?" issue. The way each person answers the question "What is real?" determines who they are and how they think. Life is a search for meaning, for truth. Albert Einstein said, "Our longing for understanding is eternal." This and survival are the driving forces that underlie our very being. Or you could say, "What difference does it make?" and simply live life for the fun of it; certainly, when it comes to lifestyles, there are many ways to skin the cat. Even so, I think everyone, on some level, seeks the truth; everyone would like to be able to tell the difference between fact and fiction. So let's take a few minutes and examine the history of this dichotomy; the difference between the real and the unreal is intriguing.

From Aristotle to Galileo, scholars down through the ages have described reality as a duality. In philosophy, it can be traced to a view that the world consists of two fundamental entities, mind and matter. In psychology, it is the phenomenalogical distinction between mental and physical processes. In theology, it is the concept that the world is ruled by antagonistic forces of good and evil embodied in heaven and hell, God and Satan; that man has two basic natures, physical and spiritual. Aristotle (384–322 B.C.) described the world as consisting of the non-material and the material. The nonmaterial was God and the material was earth, water, air, and fire. Seven hundred years later, Saint Augustine (A.D. 354–430) divided reality into the heavenly and the earthly. The heavenly was the City of God, the residence of the soul. The earthly was the City of Man, the residence of the body. The Mongols in A.D. 1200 believed

Opposite: Ron Church photo

all things were either form or matter. They invented Tai Chi, which seeks to establish harmony between the two. During the Renaissance, Galileo Galilei (A.D. 1564–1642) redefined reality as what is imagined and what is matter or energy. The imagined existed only in the mind, while matter and energy existed, absolutely in fact, outside the mind. This duality, as expressed by all these great thinkers, forms the basis of our thinking today. I suggest that it is confusion between the two that leads to the inability of many people to separate fact from fiction.

You may be saying to yourself, So what? If you are, you might want to skip the rest of this chapter. But for readers who find this discussion interesting, let me develop the subject a bit further. I agree with most of the ancient philosophers that all things can be separated into two spheres: what actually exists and what we think exists—matter and energy or simply ideas. The confusion, and the problem, lies with the realm of ideas. Some ideas are perceptions of what actually exists, such as a table or a mountain. If all human beings were to instantly die, the table and the mountain would still be there. Their existence does not depend on a human brain to perceive them. They are not the sole product of ideas, though they can exist in a person's mind. Fossils are an even better example. Fossils that were preserved before human beings evolved on this planet exist without a mind to perceive them. What about ideas of things that may or may not exist? God, for example. For people who believe in God, their idea of God is what is real. They believe it to be so. Their belief makes it true regardless of whether it is true. The belief cannot be tested. It is what they want to believe. Pure and simple.

So what is the problem? The problem arises when you want to know the absolute truth. Many people don't care if their ideas are true or false; whatever "works" is what counts. Whatever feels good is what matters. It is all about mind over matter. It "works" because of the powerful feedback mechanisms that connect the body to the mind. If you are sick but believe you will get well, it may actually help your body heal. Eventually, you may get well anyway, which can be taken as "proof" that mind over matter works. But does it really? Many people believe in prayer, miracles, spiritual forces, extrasensory perception, fatalism, UFOs, ghosts, or whatever. Many of us, though, want to be able to think critically and to tell fact from fiction. How else in the world can we deal with hallucinations, hearsay, testimonials, agendas, propaganda, manipulation of information, and so on? For this, there must be a touchstone of reality to determine the truth and point the way toward telling the difference between actual reality and virtual reality, between matter and mind. Knowing the truth is important. It may make you miserable at first, but eventually it will set you free. If our longing for understanding really is eternal, we will never rest until we find it.

For me, truth has always been one of my personal rules of life. Truth is not what I want to believe. It is not wishful thinking. It is not something I made up or something someone else made up. The truth for me must be based on more than ideas—there must be some solid evidence. This rule has been vital to my survival riding big waves. It is also vital to conducting good science. It is my existential centerpiece. It is a thought process that helps me decide at every step along the way what is real and what isn't. And the ocean helped me to distinguish the difference.

When a child dies, it is not the will of a God who works in wondrous ways. When a child lives, it is not a supernatural force that sustains it. It is a natural force. There is a cause for every effect. Things are not "meant to be." It is up to us to figure it out, to understand, and, to whatever extent possible, to control.

Having established that common sense is simply a matter of no nonsense, we must nevertheless acknowledge the heart. Life is sacred. We all find it difficult to rationalize the death of someone close. When Eddie Aikau was lost at sea, I hoped that his spirit would live on. Today, it is good to feel his power in a turtle. Memory is a form of immortality. But in the end, dust does return to dust. There is power in understanding this.

It is true, however, that all things are connected. Even the unreal can be perceived and can therefore be defined as real. To be is to be perceived. Not to be, of course, is out of the question. Keep surfing.

20 LIFE AT THE END OF THE TUNNEL

The closer you come to death, the more you appreciate life.   *Rick Grigg*

Riding big surf requires you to put your life on the line. I've been there many times during wipeouts, knowing I was only seconds away from drowning. The title of Greg Noll's book *Da Bull: Life Over the Edge* expresses the feeling well. All the big-wave riders have been there. Exactly how close do we come to death when we ride the big ones? Is it seconds away, as I imagine, or is there a wider margin of error? The time between successive big waves is about fifteen to twenty seconds. If a surfer wipes out during a big set, he must get back to the surface before the next wave passes over. A few seconds might be gained by being dragged shoreward, but you can't count on this. If you don't make it back to the surface in at least twenty seconds, chances are good that you will drown. The power of really big waves is explosive, but it is also short lived. The hold-downs on a big wave are usually only ten to fifteen seconds, maybe less. Few big-wave riders have drowned from a hold-down. A few have in recent years, though, and some of them were men in peak physical strength. Donny Solomon and Todd Chesser, two of the top surfers in the world, drowned under big waves.

Tragic losses like these tell us how close we are to death when we ride big surf. They also shed light on why anyone would risk it in the first place. The closer you come to death, the more you appreciate life. Some describe it as an adrenaline rush, almost an addiction. Flirting with death has a way of keeping you alert. It certainly is a way to avoid a life of quiet desperation. Life on the edge is about as exciting as it can get. But being there is about more than simply seeking a thrill. It gives you a sense of immortality, possibly a false one but a fleeting sense that death is impossible. Suddenly, life is filled with more meaning. It is another reason why we take the risk.

Robin and me in Waikīkī, about 1959. Clarence Maki photo.

Opposite: Ron Church photo.

Then there is the sheer thrill of it. How does it feel to ride a 25- or 30- or even 35-foot wave? The skills required take years to develop. The physical training involves strength, agility, endurance, and breath holding—many seasons and thousands of waves to tune the senses. The wave and ocean knowledge are gained only with experience—knowledge of lineups, currents, reef layout, and depths unique to each surfing break. Years go into making each critical decision: how to get out, where to sit on the lineup, what kind of board to ride, seeing a set early, jockeying for position, and then picking the wave. Judgment is the key to being in the right place at the right time.

Commitment is part of the equation, too. You tell yourself to take off. This is it. The moment of truth. You put your life on the line and go for it. In one minute you could be dead or you might be flying out of a tunnel big enough to drive a Mack truck through. Can you make it? Will you make it? When you do, the world explodes in elation around you. You did it. Your legs are trembling with adrenaline. And when you get wiped out? Then there is the elation and relief of having survived a hold-down that could have killed you. Either way, the light at the end of this kind of tunnel feels like immortality.

Looking back at my life from the end of the tunnel, I see the ocean as my teacher. Unending struggle always faced me—the choice between freedom or responsibility, to be myself or to follow the rules, to be a scientist or to be a surfer, to escape or to join, to take or to give. The ocean always helped me determine my priorities. It is a source of wisdom. It is the maker of natural laws. Out on the ocean, I could feel like a flying fish but no more important. What mattered was the physical vigor of being alive. Survival was the purpose. It is simple, logical, and true.

So how was I to combine being a selfish rogue with having a desire to meet the needs of others? A social instinct pulled me away from myself, back toward the group. I knew their rules were just as made up as my own, but there were some I could not ignore. To be more than I could be alone, I had to join and give way to others. The anti-establishment of the 1960s had made the same discoveries and helped me understand the unsanctity of the social order.

The ocean had steeled me to be independent and to be myself, but it had not taught me much about respecting the rights of others. Riding 25-foot waves had given me great elation and even a fleeting sense of immortality, but it did not fulfill the social contract. For that I would depend on my family and my friends. I would always remind myself, it is the heart that counts the most.

Last, I had to learn to follow the rules, even though they were not my own. Learning this lesson helped me become a marine scientist and a family man. It allowed me to live under the sea—to dive to great depths

My daughter Carol on safari in Africa, a trip we took together.

172

Above right: My daughter Raina with her first surfboard, and learning to swim.

Below right: My grandson Titus gearing up for his first wave.

and study reefs and islands all over the world. It also gave me three wives, three daughters, a stepdaughter and stepson, and happiness I would never have known alone.

My family is about as complicated as it could be. My mom passed away in 1976 at age sixty-nine. She is the one who, more than any other, made it all happen for me—the romance, the adventure, the advice to "be yourself" and to be honest and never to be shy about speaking my mind. Today, my sister Robin lives on her ranch in Honoka'a, on the Big Island. My daughter Raina now has a young son Titus and lives in La Jolla, California. My second wife, Carol, lives in Hawai'i and has three daughters, Julie, Romy, and Jamie—Romy is our daughter, who lives and works in La Jolla. My third wife, Maria, was born in the Philippines, and her son (now our son), Mark, is from her first marriage. My high school sweetheart, Pat Davis, and I have a daughter, Carol, who is married and lives in Sacramento and has two sons, Ryan and Eric. It is a chop-suey mixture, but remarkably, we have come pretty close to being one big, happy family. Of course, like any family we have our problems, but we blend amazingly well, and each and every one has a special place in my heart.

Life at the end of the tunnel is what you make it. For me, it has been an accumulation of my dreams: big surf, deep dives, the islands, and

REFLECTIONS FROM A DAUGHTER
by Raina Grigg

In the glare of an afternoon sun and the mist from 8-foot breakers, I see my aging dad, his chin and chest thrust into the surf. He is sixty-one now. His five-year-old grandson plays on the beach, as I did in my own childhood. I am one of his daughters, his prodigy, his genetic immortality. I am Raina.

Jack London wrote, "A wave is a communicated agitation." My sisters and I could say the same about my father. He is a passionate, intense man. Masculinity and the surfing brotherhood are extremely important to him. Having daughters and loving women are emotional paradoxes for him, from which he escapes into the ocean. Unlike his marriages, communication with the waves is easy. He either makes the wave or he doesn't.

Dad is controversial within his surfing and science brotherhood. He is respected but not always accepted. Many of his friends bite their tongue to avoid a confrontation. Nevertheless, no matter what comes his way, Dad remains amazingly joyful from one adventure to the next. He has the unique ability to inspire us and help us pursue our dreams.

PUKA - SHELL NECKLACES
from: SUNSET BEACH HAWAII

SEND:
neck size and $20.00
(cash, check or mon. order)

TO:

The PACIFIC OCEAN Co.
59-071 Hoalua st.
Sunset Beach
Hawaii 96712

Carol, Julie, and Romy pose for a puka-shell ad for Surfer *magazine. Julie found the shells and Carol made the necklaces.*

Julie is now a glamour photography artist in Hollywood.

Romy in junior high school, where she excelled in gymnastics and dance.

romance. The romance is with life. My philosophy of life has always been simple: Follow your heart, be purely honest and let integrity be your guide. And above all, keep surfing. The ocean taught me these rules by shaping my feelings and perceptions. It helped me answer the "who" and "why" questions about life. The ocean has also given me a deep sense of humility. For this I am reminded of a Piet Hein poem I learned as a small boy: "The noble art of losing face / May someday save the human race / And turn into eternal merit / What weaker minds would call disgrace."

One day my ashes will mingle with those of Eddie Aikau, Jose Angel, Mark Foo, and Rell Sunn in the ocean waters of the Hawaiian Islands. Perhaps together, with help from the turtles, we will guide new surfers to the place where they can catch the waves. There, in the surf, we will all swim together for a long, long time to come.

My third wife, Maria, and my stepson
Mark. Maria was born in the Philip-
pines. Mark is the genius of the family.

Maria and me at sunset at our
Sunset home: our life at the
end of the tunnel.

RICK GRIGG CHRONOLOGY

BORN	April 12, 1937
1946	Began surfing
1953	First trip to Hawai'i
1954	Graduated from Santa Monica High School
1955	Won first Catalina to Manhattan Beach paddleboard race, 32 miles
1956	Graduated from Santa Monica City College
1958	Graduated from Stanford University
1958	Moved to Hawai'i to ride big waves on the North Shore
1959	Sailed to Tahiti on board the *Maunawanui*
1964	Master's degree from the University of Hawai'i
1964	Entered Scripps Institution of Oceanography
1965	*Sea Lab II;* Meritorious Public Service Award from the Secretary of the Navy
1967	Won second Duke Kahanamoku International Surfing Invitational
1970	Ph.D. from Scripps Institution of Oceanography
1970	Joined faculty of the University of Hawai'i, Department of Oceanography
1972–1978	Research on Hawai'i's precious corals
1980	Discovered the Darwin Point, where Hawaiian Islands drown
1987	Among first team of scientists in history to dive on Lō'ihi Seamount, the next Hawaiian Island
1987	Kanaka O Ke Kai Ocean Recognition Award, Honolulu, Hawai'i
1990–1995	Managing Editor of the journal *Coral Reefs*
1991–1997	Member, National Committee of the Pacific Science Association, U.S. National Academy of Sciences
1995	Inducted into Santa Monica High School's Hall of Fame for surfing and distinction in education
1996	Finalist, Charles Darwin Gold Medal, International Society for Reef Studies, Panama City, Panama
1970–2000	Professor of Oceanography, University of Hawai'i
1997	Voted one of "Ninety Illustrious Alumni of the University of Hawai'i," in celebration of its 90th Anniversary, 1907–1997
2000	Still surfing (I hope)

GLOSSARY

Capillary waves. Tiny ripples with wavelengths less than 0.7 inches. The first waves to form when the wind blows.

Convergence. Concentration of wave energy (height) when wave crests bend inward toward a center point (increases wave height).

Decay. Decrease in wave height due to distance traveled.

Dispersion. Separation of waves of different wavelengths caused by differences in speed.

Divergence. Spreading of wave energy when wave crests bend outward away from a center point (lowers wave height).

Duration. Time a storm remains in the same area.

Fetch. Distance the wind blows over the water.

Group velocity. Speed of a wave train; half the speed of individual waves.

Orbital velocity. Rotational speed of water particles resulting from the passage of a wave.

Phase velocity. Speed of individual waves.

Period. Time between two waves passing a fixed point.

Refraction. Bending of wave crests in shallow water.

Rogue wave. Exceptional wave, up to 2.5 times larger than significant waves.

Sea. Waves of all wavelengths within a storm, forming a chaotic surface.

Sets. A group of waves that travel together because of a common wavelength.

Significant waves. ($H_{1/3}$) Average height of the upper one-third of all waves in a given storm.

Shoaling. The process of waves traveling into shallow water.

Swell. Smooth, deepwater waves after they leave a fetch area in a storm.

Wave length. Distance between two successive wave crests.

Wave height. Vertical distance between the crest and the trough of a wave.

Wave crest. Highest part of a wave.

Wave trough. Lowest part of a wave.

NAME INDEX